traces of guilt

forensic science
and the fight against crime

Hugh Miller

BBC Books

This book is published to
accompany the television series
entitled *Traces of Guilt* which
was first broadcast in 1995
EXECUTIVE PRODUCER:
Caroline van den Brul
SERIES PRODUCER:
David Sington
PRODUCERS:
Mary Fitzpatrick, Isabelle Rosin,
Henry Singer, Colleen Toomey

Published by BBC Books,
an imprint of BBC Worldwide
Publishing
BBC Worldwide Limited,
Woodlands, 80 Wood Lane,
London W12 0TT

First published 1995
© Hugh Miller, 1995
The moral right of the author has
been asserted

ISBN 0 563 36964 7

DESIGNED BY Bobby Birchall,
Town Group Consultancy

Set in Helvetica Neue

Printed and bound in Great Britain
by Clays Ltd, St Ives plc

Colour separations by Dot
Gradations, South Woodham
Ferrers, Nr Chelmsford

Introduction 6

1 **The Company of Strangers** 10

2 **Mad or Bad** 40

3 **Buried Witnesses** 68

contents

4 **White Collars, White Coats** 92

5 **The Secret War** 124

6 **The Verdict** 156

Index 190

intro duction

'Every contact leaves a trace' is the creed of those who scour the scene of a crime for evidence linking the criminal to his acts. Though today's SOCOs (scene-of-crime officers) work clad in sterile one-piece boiler suits and plastic gloves rather than deerstalkers, they are heirs to a tradition that begins with Sherlock Holmes. Like the fictional sleuth of Baker Street, their task is minutely to examine the crime scene for anything the criminal may have brought to it. Blood, semen, saliva, hair, clothing fibres, cigarette butts, fingerprints, footprints, tyre marks, cartridge cases, scratches left by jemmies or other tools, bitemarks, even sweat – all have been successfully used to convict felons in courtrooms around the world.

This is the traditional territory staked out by forensic science and the techniques that lie at the heart of *Traces of Guilt*. Yet there is a lot more to forensic science and forensic scientists than the examination of these contact traces. Today, many forensic scientists are questioning the scientific basis of what they do while others feel frustrated with what happens to their evidence in the courtroom. Some are using their talents not in the fight against everyday crime, but in the worldwide struggle for human rights. Sometimes the interesting scientific question is not who did it, but why, and the answer to this question can mean the difference between life and death for the criminal involved.

'The Company of Strangers' tells the story of how a horrifying series of murders in Europe and the United States was proved to be the work of one person, Jack Unterweger, a successful Austrian writer and broadcaster who claimed the dubious distinction of being the world's first known international serial killer.

Serial murderers are among the most difficult of criminals to catch, for a very simple reason. They kill strangers, and by doing so they wittingly or unwittingly render traditional forensic science useless.

Most murder investigations are based on what detectives call 'victimology', the study of the victim's circumstances, lifestyle, habits and so forth. This victimology will usually yield someone who had a motive for the killing. The investigation will then focus on this suspect and it is at this stage that any physical evidence collected at the crime scene comes into play. But if the victim met the killer for the first time only hours, or even minutes before the crime, this approach does not work. It does not matter how much physical evidence the police have – without a suspect to relate it to it is of little help to their investigation.

The good news is that forensic science is beginning to rise to the challenge – the answer lies in the use of computer databases. Databases of fingerprints are well established, of course, and they make fingerprints a uniquely useful form of physical evidence, because a print found at a crime scene can be compared with those stored in a computer. This can link unsolved crimes together, and even sometimes tell the police whom they should arrest. DNA databases are in the process of being set up, and in the future they are sure to provide a potent tool, especially in sexual crimes, where the perpetrators are often repeat offenders with criminal records.

'Mad or Bad' examines a deep-seated problem that bedevils the relationship between science and the law. What happens when experts disagree? The cases in point are two murders, committed by two different people, where the facts of the matter are not in dispute. The question which the jury has to decide is whether or not the killer was responsible for his actions at the time he killed.

Scientific experts are, of course, expected to provide an objective opinion which will guide the jury to make an informed decision. In the first case, two psychiatrists who have examined the accused disagree in their assessment of his state of mind when he killed. In the second, the psychiatrists for the prosecution and defence agree so the accused's lawyers – knowing that he would face the death penalty if this psychiatric evidence was presented in court – simply search elsewhere in science for their defence. They find it in an unlikely place: neuroscience. This story exposes the difficulties faced by judges and juries who are charged with assessing the validity of scientific evidence presented to them in court. How is a non-specialist jury to decide between the testimonies of two experts who fundamentally disagree?

'Buried Witnesses' delves into the area of human rights abuses. Here, there is little disagreement about what the forensic scientists find, but their work is ignored by the justice system because of political pressures. Dr Clyde Snow is an American forensic pathologist turned anthropologist who has developed forensic archaeology as a powerful tool. We follow him and his team as they excavate the remains of a village in the hills of Guatemala whose entire population was massacred in 1982. Their painstaking exhumations and laboratory analysis discover that the Guatemalan government was behind the killings, information it has not surpisingly chosen to suppress. By bringing the world's attention to such events, Clyde Snow hopes to convince killers that they can no longer hide their guilt. They say history is written by the winners, but Dr Snow believes that with the help of science, history can be truth.

'White Collars, White Coats' enters a world inhabited by document examiners and typewriting experts who cast their experienced eyes over diaries, expense claims, wills and deeds to identify forgeries. And if this is a world which seems to be fast disappearing, new white-collar crimes are springing up to take its place, such as computer crime and the theft of cellular telephones. These new scourges, which can affect us all, show how forensic scientists are engaged in cat-and-mouse games with increasingly ingenious and sophisticated criminals. The scientists must not only keep track of forgeries but stay one step ahead. They are not always altogether successful.

Another area of criminal activity which increasingly affects us, directly or indirectly, is the manufacture and importation of illegal drugs. Here, too, scientists and criminals play a complex and dangerous game. 'The Secret War' looks at how the battle against drug importation is being fought and highlights the important strategic role played by the forensic scientists.

'The Verdict' covers perhaps the most important single issue gnawing at the image of forensic science today: the reliability of scientific evidence presented to the courts. It examines the case of a man convicted of murder almost solely on the testimony of a disreputable forensic odontologist (dentist) and reveals that much of the scientific evidence presented in court has little foundation in science. Techniques which mainstream scientists would reject as unreliable are presented in court as evidence of a person's guilt or innocence. Many of the techniques (analysis of hair, fibres, toolmarks, handwriting, ballistics, etc) which forensic scientists use have never been subjected to strict scientific appraisal. Ironically, one of the exceptions to this is DNA profiling, often the branch of forensic science that the public considers most problematic due to the publicity it has had in recent years. This publicity has, in fact, been the result of the gradual evolution and improvement of the science. For DNA analysis, unlike many branches of forensics, grew out of mainstream twentieth-century science. When it transferred to the forensic arena it continued to be subjected to scientific rigour. The time is ripe for such reform in other branches of forensic science.

This story stands as a cautionary tale for forensic scientists, police officers, lawyers and all of us concerned that justice be served. Forensic science can be a powerful tool, but when it is misused it can devastate innocent lives. *Traces of Guilt* explores the use of forensic science in our society and raises searching questions about its role in law enforcement. The examples we have highlighted have profound implications for criminal justice systems around the world.

Caroline van den Brul

the company of stran

Malibu is an exclusive beach community in Los Angeles, on the Pacific Coastal Highway, west-northwest of Santa Monica. It is an unusually attractive and secluded colony, situated where the Santa Monica mountains meet the ocean. The residents, many of whom are film and television personalities, have built their homes along an escarpment overlooking the picturesque Santa Monica Bay.

On 11 July 1991, a partial eclipse of the sun was visible from Malibu. Two men who had come out to witness the spectacle stood on a steep hill overlooking the bay, watching the sky through dark-tinted glasses. As the wind shifted they were aware suddenly of a terrible putrid smell, like a whiff from a backed-up sewer. They approached the spot where the stench seemed to come from and found the black and swollen body of a young woman, lying in brushwood. She was wearing jeans, trainers, and a T-shirt pulled up exposing her breasts, and had apparently been strangled with her bra.

gers

The police were alerted and within a few minutes a team from the LA County Sheriff's Office, led by Ron Lancaster, were at the scene. As the body and the surrounding area were photographed and crime-scene specimens were collected, officers speculated about whether the victim was a prostitute; they hoped she was not, because when a working girl is murdered, it's nearly always by someone she didn't know. If there is no relationship between victim and killer then there is nothing to limit the circle of potential suspects; the murder could have been committed by anyone, and is therefore the most difficult kind to solve.

Crime detection before the nineteenth century was vastly different from present-day systems and procedures, not merely because of the absence of forensic science and technology, but because people lived in small and largely self-regulating communities. Everyone knew his neighbour, strangers in town stood out clearly and changes in individual trends of behaviour did too. So serious crime, in the main, was easy to detect and to solve. There were no professional detectives, and little investigation of crime in the modern sense.

The Industrial Revolution changed all this. Smaller communities became linked by commerce, cities grew, and for the first time people began conducting their lives surrounded by strangers. Inevitably crime flourished. In places like London and Birmingham it reached crisis proportions. Necessity produced the first professional police forces, and the detective arrived on the scene.

These now professional investigators soon realized that they needed new techniques for identifying who among the mass of anonymous faces in the new cities were responsible for the burglaries, muggings and murders that were becoming distressingly common. The identities of people, in the day-to-day sense, are forged in their interactions with family, friends and workmates. This social network defines who a person is. Where a criminal is an unrecognized stranger, his social identity is unknown.

So a new science of *physical identity* had to be developed.

Experience soon made it clear that the first step to establishing a criminal's identity lay in a close examination of the crime scene. In Great Britain and America, a formal system of training in this work was advocated by police authorities at local and national levels. (Among the advocates was Sir Arthur Conan Doyle, who championed detailed scene-of-crime analysis in his Sherlock Holmes stories.)

As crime-scene examination was put on an organized basis and began to develop, observers of law enforcement predicted that detailed investigation of contact traces – marks left by the felon – would be one major area where criminal detection would expand and flourish.

Where there is a particular scientific need, there is usually someone who can define it thoroughly and fill the gap. The person in this case was Alphonse Bertillon, who, from 1880, was chief of criminal investigation for the Paris police. In 1882 Bertillon introduced his system of physical identification. The technique was described as anthropometric – comparative human-body computations – and it incorporated a series of refined body measurements, physical descriptions and photographs. Collectively these furnished an excellent means of arriving at a detailed picture of an individual, and the system was adopted by Scotland Yard as a standard for profiling and identification. But in the end the unwieldy nature of the Bertillon technique simply highlighted the need for a simple and fast method of physical identification.

Throughout the final years of the nineteenth century extensive research went into the criminal-classification possibilities of fingerprints. A contemporary German scientific journal observed that:

Oily impressions left on smooth surfaces by the ridges on the ends of the fingers and thumbs are foreseeably of use as a means of identification of different persons, since it is now believed that no two persons display the same pattern of ridges.

As research went forward it was found that any ridged area of the hand or foot could be used for identification. Fingerprints would be best, however, since they were the kind most often left behind at a crime scene, and they could be checked against suspects' fingertips with a minimum of difficulty.

The Galton–Henry system of fingerprint classification was published in 1900. In 1902 it was introduced at Scotland Yard, displacing Bertillon's anthropometric system as the primary method for creating criminal investigation records. In a very short time the Galton–Henry system was adopted by scores of law enforcement agencies around the world, and it remains the most widely used system of fingerprint classification.

The invention of another original technique for classifying fingerprints, this one by Juan Vucetich, was overshadowed by the Galton–Henry system, but it was nevertheless an effective method which might have gained acceptance had it not been for the relative simplicity of the other method.

Vucetich, an Argentinian, was a police employee in Buenos Aires. In 1888 he published a book called *Dactiloscopia Comparada* (Comparative Fingerprinting). The method he devised involved cleaning the fingertips with benzene or ether, drying them, then rolling the balls of the fingers over a sheet of glass coated with printer's ink. Each finger was then rolled on a prepared card, according to a precise technique, which produced a light grey impression with clear spaces visible between the ridges; the ridges could then be individually traced and counted. The method was almost immediately assigned to the category of Significant Historical Developments, but it stands, all the same, as a testament to the skill and ingenuity that marked nineteenth-century scientific invention.

As fingerprinting became a standard technique in everyday crime detection, there were inevitable refinements. A system of classification for loops and whorls was developed, and all the characteristics were subdivided into types – e.g. Loop, Double Loop and Central Pocket Loop; Plain Whorl; Plain Arch, Tented

Arch. The technique of taking prints from individuals was improved, and so were the various methods of revealing finger marks at the scene of a crime. Today fingerprints are classified via a three-way process: by general shapes and contours; by the positions of the pattern types on the fingers; and by the relative size, which is determined by counting the ridges in loops and by tracing ridges in whorls. It is this systematic classification of fingerprints which makes it possible to search a large database of stored prints of known criminals for a match with one from the scene of a crime.

Early on, it was accepted as a fact that no two fingerprints could be the same. But that cannot be proved. All that can be said is that with such variety in number, placement and configuration of loops and whorls on the fingers of human beings, the chances of two remotely similar prints turning up near each other is fantastically unlikely.

But the law needs something as near as possible to a certainty, since a matter of probability, however clearly stated, is still technically vague. Much research therefore went into determining how many points of similarity between two prints would be needed, on careful examination, to make a chance match so improbable that it would be virtually certain that two prints, so matched, would have come from the same individual. Some authorities eventually accepted 16 as the crucial number of similarities, others accept 12. Minor reservations aside, the present system of fingerprint classification is held to be exceptionally reliable.

Back in Malibu, the decomposed body of the murdered woman was taken from the hillside to the city mortuary in downtown Los Angeles. Fingerprints were taken and then, in line with current practice, the print images were digitized. This involved a scanner head being passed over the prints to convert the unique arrangements of loops, arches and whorls into numeric information, which could be processed by a computer much faster than pictorial data.

The prints were then submitted to comparison with millions of others which are held in the California fingerprint computer database. Within a short time the numeric information from the dead woman's prints made a match with a set of figures in the database. The computer reversed the conversion and turned the numeric information into a picture, showing the print taken at the mortuary alongside the matching print held on record. The print belonged to Sherry Long, 25 years old, a prostitute.

So in all probability this was the worst-case scenario, a stranger killing. Details of the case, initially handled by the LA Sheriff's Department, had to be communicated to the LAPD, which shares the responsibility for policing Los Angeles with the Sheriff's Department and other units. The routine teletype from Ron Lancaster eventually reached the hands of Jim Harper, a homicide detective with the LAPD. When Harper read the information about the dead woman, it rang alarm bells. He had seen two similar killings of females in the previous month: both women were prostitutes, both brutally strangled, their naked bodies dumped on waste ground. Another feature common to the three crimes was that the women had been strangled with their own bras, which had been knotted and wound tightly around their necks.

The three bras were taken for comparison to Lynn Herrold of the LA County Crime Laboratory. Herrold is a criminalist, a professional whose job is to apply the physical sciences to the detection of crime. Each year she examines countless pieces of evidence from thousands of crimes. She regards her work as largely puzzle-solving.

Ligatures used for strangulation are a particular enthusiasm, and Herrold teaches scene-of-crime officers how to remove them from bodies. Since the way a knot is tied can often indicate who committed the murder, the knot is never untied: instead, the ligature is cut close to the knot, leaving it intact. This had been done with the bras. When Lynn Herrold examined them she found that they had been expertly stripped down to act as lethal garrottes. It was inconceivable, she said, that more than one person had committed

these crimes. The police obviously had a serial killer on their hands.
The term 'serial killer' was coined by Special Agent Robert Ressler
of the FBI Behavioural Sciences Unit at Quantico, Virginia, the place
from which national statistics for crime in the USA are issued – the
particular department is Uniform Crime Reports (UCR). The annual
report, Crime in the United States, provides valuable source
material for criminologists and social psychologists, as well as law
enforcers anxious to detect and curtail trends in crime. The UCR
also provides annual data on the incidence of crimes in the five
categories of murder specified by the FBI. The categories are as
follows.

Felony murder (committed during the commission of
another crime).
Suspected felony murder (elements of felony are
detectable).
Argument-motivated murder (not as a result of criminal
intent).
Other motives (any motive not included in the foregoing
categories).
Unknown motives (motive fits none of the foregoing
categories).

The absence of any known link between victim and killer – as in
the case of Sherry Long – tends to put a case into the category of
'unknown motives'. But sexual murder, in particular, although it is
sharply motivated, often seems random and without motive. This is
especially the case when the killer deliberately chooses a victim he
does not know, and then conceals the sexual basis of the killing. A
considerable number of such cases are automatically classified as
being of unknown motive.

During the past 15 years, figures for most categories of motive
have remained reasonably steady; the exception is the 'unknown'
category, which has shown a tremendous increase.

The numbers and the incidence of sexual murders are hard to

pin down and solving them is difficult, mainly for the reasons given above. In the unknown motive category there are many so-called serial killings, and tied to that fact is another: both investigators and clinical experts believe that serial killings are sexual in nature.

The conclusion is that sexually motivated serial killing is on the increase at a disturbing rate. Among those who scientifically evaluate serial murderers, the term 'multiple-victim murderer' is now more commonly used.

'It was a matter of finding a cover-all term,' says an English researcher. 'Multiple-victim killers are usually called either mass murderers or serial killers. A mass murderer is taken to be someone who kills a number of people all at once, whereas a serial killer does it over a relatively long period of time.'

Richard Speck, who killed eight nurses in their Chicago dormitory in a single night in 1966, was described in the press as a mass murderer; when James Huberty shot and killed 21 people at a McDonald's in San Ysidro, California, he was called a mass murderer, too. Ted Bundy, believed to have committed 34 murders over a four-year period, was labelled a serial killer.

'There don't appear to be important psychological differences between mass murderers and serial killers,' a psychiatrist said. 'The important distinction is between the subjects who kill only once, and those who kill several times.'

In spite of the increase in their numbers, multiple-victim killers are still quite rare, and there is consequently a shortage of detailed information about background influences and motivation. Figures from the US Department of Justice, and others, suggest there were approximately 32 active serial killers in the USA during the period 1970–85. The figures for mass murderers are similarly low. Also, because multiple-victim killers attract such a volume of sensational publicity, serious students and researchers tend to avoid them; good case studies are consequently scarce.

An English psychiatrist says that the general public is more likely to perceive a serial killer or mass murderer as a human incarnation of sheer evil, than as a disturbed and possibly psychotic person.

'That's thanks to the press, of course,' she says. 'They paint these violently emotive pictures and have no regard at all, or very little, for the sombre and often sad truth underlying the sensational facts of a case.'

In their 1985 American study *Mass Murder*, J. Levin and J. Fox (respectively a sociologist and a professor of criminal justice) pointed out that certain studies of multiple-victim killers were based on subject-samples which were too small to be without some measure of bias. In an effort to produce a bigger and therefore more accurate sampling, Levin and Fox gathered information on 42 multiple-victim killers and their crimes; the data were supplemented by conversations with judges, attorneys and other professionals connected with many of the cases, and the authors even spoke to a few of the killers. In the resulting study they presented a composite profile of the typical multiple-victim killer. Two British psychiatrists have produced similar profiles, and the following is an abridged composite of their findings:

The typical multiple-victim killer is a white man in his late twenties or early thirties. In cases of mass murder (i.e. when all the victims are killed on the same occasion), he uses a handgun or a rifle to kill people he knows. When committing serial murders he kills strangers by beating or strangling them. Reasons for the killings are governed by the circumstances which precipitate the crime, but commonly the motive is A: financial; B: a means of obtaining an otherwise impossible end; C: jealousy; D: an overpowering but unfocused sexual urge. Although the multiple-victim killer may seen abnormally cool and detached about his actions, and he may express no remorse for what he has

done, signs of psychosis or other mental illness are usually absent.

Levin and Fox concluded that most multiple-victim killers are 'more evil than crazy', and that they are very severe sociopathic personalities.

In criminology and abnormal psychology, an objective understanding often emerges from a study of the facts of cases considered side by side. The following seven short case summaries may give an idea of the range of human types and circumstances central to the phenomenon of multiple-victim killing.

Case 1

David was left by his mother in the care of an alcoholic aunt when he was six. From the age of seven until he was technically no longer a child, David was in trouble with the police and the juvenile authorities for theft, running away from home, truancy and a couple of minor instances of arson.

He married when he was 22 and settled into steady employment as a welder in an engineering works. When he was 24 he had the first of several psychotic episodes and believed that Christ appeared to him regularly, usually at meal breaks at work when David sat alone at the back of a workshop to eat his sandwiches. He was told by Christ that he must purify a certain hilltop in preparation for the second (highly public) coming of the messiah. Purification had to be by fire, which was complicated by the fact that a small observatory stood on the top of the hill.

David went straight to the director of the observatory and told him he should get himself and his staff well away from the place, because it had to be destroyed. When the director threatened to call the police, David went away. He returned an hour later with a stolen shotgun, a box of cartridges and a can of petrol. He marched into the director's office and said if he didn't leave he would be shot. At that point the director's secretary made a run for it (and was subsequently able to give the story to the police), but the director stood his ground. David shot him though the chest, then went through the building and shot the other six people he found there. He then doused the hallways with petrol and was still attempting to burn the place when the police arrived and arrested him.

A psychiatrist diagnosed David as suffering from paranoid schizophrenia. At his trial he was found to be sane and was sent to prison for life.

Case 2

Erich, a German boy, was an adopted child whose mother was alternately harsh and smotheringly kind to him from childhood right into his early twenties. At times when his mother punished him she was prone to tell him that his natural mother was a whoring Berlin slut that any man could have for the price of a drink. It was not unusual for Erich to find himself pampered and cuddled and given sweets when he came home from school, then be held on his mother's knee while they watched TV together until his bedtime; next morning, his mother would refuse to speak to him, make him get his own breakfast, and even withhold small sums of money needed for routine contributions at school.

When Erich's adoptive father died (Erich was 14) the mother told him she expected him to start supporting her as soon as he could. Erich eventually joined the police force as a cadet. He failed some of his examinations and was unable to continue in a police career; instead, he switched to private security and was employed as a patrol guard by a firm specializing in estate and factory-perimeter security.

A year after beginning security work Erich moved in with a girl he had known only three weeks and they proceeded to live as man and wife, eventually producing a child. During the same period Erich raped and strangled 12 young women in and around Berlin. He was eventually caught and several psychiatrists ventured the opinion that Erich suffered from a multiple personality disorder; an examining judge did not accept that and Erich was declared sane and fit to stand trial. He was sentenced to life imprisonment.

The Company of Strangers

Case 3

Betty, a black woman living in Reno, Nevada, had been a patient in several psychiatric hospitals by the time she reached her 52nd birthday. In her mid-forties she had been diagnosed as suffering from paranoid schizophrenia; her delusions were religious, among them a conviction that she was a new incarnation of Jesus Christ. (It is relatively common for schizophrenic women to believe they are Christ.)

Betty had been married several times and had a daughter by her third marriage. The child had been taken from her and placed in a foster home when Mary was 45 and the child was three. On Thanksgiving Day, 1980, when the child would be ten years old, Mary felt herself unusually oppressed at the loss of her daughter and her 'religious persecution'. A witness had described her mood as 'dark, the darkest yet'.

That afternoon Betty drove her car along the pavement of a street in a busy commercial sector of Reno. She ran over and killed six people and injured 23 more.

At her trial Betty was found sane. In 1982 she became the first black woman to be given the death sentence in the United States since the death penalty had been reinstated. More than 14 years later, Betty is still on Death Row.

Case 4

Ed grew up in the North West United States. When he was six his parents divorced and he was profoundly affected by the upheaval this caused in his life; the upset appeared to persist into his late teens.

From an early age Ed was attracted to the erotic and was even known to have a fascination, from the age of 9, with semi-pornographic pictures (initially shown to him by older boys, then sought out by Ed on his own initiative). He was also fascinated by death and had twice been caught in the back premises of a funeral parlour near his home – once when he was 10, again when he was 11. The second time he had been found staring fixedly into a coffin where an old woman lay, powdered and shrouded for her wake.

Ed often played 'death' games. He would tiptoe into his mother's bedroom with a knife and go through a mime of killing her as she slept. He devised a mock-up gas chamber, in which he had his sister tie him to a chair, then throw an imaginary switch. Ed would pretend to die with much choking, writhing and spluttering.

Then, at the age of 15, Ed killed his maternal grandparents while staying at their ranch. He was incarcerated and released six years later. Not long afterwards he began killing and mutilating female college students. They were all notably attractive young women, the kind of college girls his mother had told him he would never be able to date. His routine was to offer two girls a lift in his car (he always picked up victims two at a time), then at a secluded spot he would shoot his passengers, decapitate them with a hunting knife and have sex with the bodies.

On Good Friday 1973, approximately a year after he began killing students, Ed killed his mother. After decapitating her, he is reported to have cut out her larynx, 'so she can never nag me again'. He then turned himself in at the local police station, feeling that he had no further need to kill. He was eventually found sane and was imprisoned for life.

Case 5

Jeremy, raised by academic parents (father a college lecturer in English, mother the same at a minor university in the English Midlands), showed an aptitude for drawing and painting in his early teens and expressed a desire to enter the theatre as a designer. He completed a design course in London in 1968 and travelled to New York to study stage design with an elite group in Manhattan. Jeremy's work impressed people and he completed two professional commissions for Broadway productions before returning to England in 1971.

He had been back less than a week, staying at the parental home until his new flat in Chelsea was decorated, when the body of a local boy was found in a field behind a pub. He had been strangled, and his tongue was missing (it was found later in a brook). There had long been a suspicion in the village that the youth was a homosexual, and a post-mortem examination of the body showed that he was probably habituated to anal intercourse. Sex had taken place close to the time of death. Prejudice and blind loyalties being what they are, the general local feeling was that some transient pervert had committed the crime – no one in the area was capable of anything so vile and besides, to quote a local police constable, 'I know these parts, and if there were any perverts in the area, apart from the one that's dead, I'd know about it'.

A detective from Birmingham, paying no attention to prejudice or to the theories that had been collected along with statements, submitted the key details of the murder (buggery, strangulation with a slip-knotted cord, mutilation) to a police collator in London, a woman with a particularly good memory for patterns of crime. Inside three days she managed to produce five cases, covering a three-year period to May 1968, of homicides, all committed in London, and all similar to the one in the Midlands – the one common factor was that the victims had had their tongues cut out.

A record of villagers' movements and all available corroborating statements soon drew the detective's attention towards Jeremy. Suspicion hardened when inquiries were made in the area of London near the flats where Jeremy had lived during his student days. His former landlady and two neighbours recalled he had a reputation for frequenting homosexual bars in the Earls Court area, and had often left the premises with young strangers he had picked up. Twice he had brought young men back with him, the landlady reported, 'and the way they went on up there, you'd have thought it was a girl he'd brought back'.

When Jeremy was questioned by the police he denied the heavy implications and insisted that a terrible mistake was being made – and, he added, it was a mistake for which someone would suffer.

Two days after he was questioned, a telex message from Edinburgh advised the detective that Jeremy had been invited to help police with their inquiries in connection with a homosexual slaying in the Leith area in the summer of 1967. The victim had been strangled and his tongue was halfway cut out. The case, at that time, remained unsolved.

Late on a November evening in 1971 the detective called at the home of Jeremy's parents and asked to see Jeremy again. The pale-faced father came out into the porch and told the detective that, four hours earlier, Jeremy had gone out for a walk. He had seemed to be in buoyant spirits when he left, but eight or ten minutes later he had crossed a nearby embankment on to a railway line and had thrown himself in front of an express train.

The village murder, the six look-alike cases from London and the one in Edinburgh were never solved, nor was the reason for the mutilations ever explained. The detective, however, had no doubt Jeremy was the murderer in all seven cases. There were too many coincidences of time and movement for the killer to have been anyone else – it had even been discovered that Jeremy was in Leith, on a course, when the murder there was committed. And apart from that, among Jeremy's boyhood notebooks was one where he had written a vividly detailed short story of a lad who caught a thief, thrashed him, then cut out his tongue – 'to stop him spreading tales to poison people's ears'.

Case 6

In the poor suburb of Frankfurt, Germany, where Otto lived with his widowed father and his grandmother, theft was a common means of occasionally improving the generally tight finances. Otto was only an averagely skilled thief, but he was very small for his years, and even at the age of ten he could squeeze through a fanlight window into a house and pass the owners' valuables out to his friends.

On one visit to a street his gang had never raided before, Otto climbed in through a tiny broken transom of an old house and found himself staring down at an old dead man on the floor. Otto had never before lost control of his emotions, except for occasionally crying a little when his father beat him, but when he saw the decomposed body in the shadowy half light of that old house, he began screaming. In later years he said that in that minute or so of screeching terror he had weakened the hinges on the door separating his sanity from the madness which, he was sure, he had carried around with him since birth.

In dreams for years afterwards he often saw the dead man, but in every dream he was not quite dead; in some he spoke words that meant nothing, in others he remained silent but his eyes blinked slowly, staring up at the transom as Otto howled and tried to scramble back outside to the safety of the street. In every dream, there was one constant feature: the old man always had a long hard penis jutting from his trousers, and Otto found that both compelling and terrifying. As he entered puberty, the dreams of the old dead man frequently merged into dream episodes of sex with a beautiful girl, and in the dream Otto always choked the girl to death as he reached his climax.

Eight days after his 15th birthday, and three days after he was released from youth custody after serving six months for aggravated burglary, Otto murdered a girl. He strangled her with her own pants while having sexual intercourse with her. He merely stretched the garment between his hands and brought the taut ligament down on her neck, working the ends into his fists and tightening the band on her throat as he climaxed.

'I had dreamed the way of doing it long before I really did it,' he told a psychiatrist. 'It was one fantasy that travelled over into the real world without disappointing me.'

The murder was poorly investigated because the girl was the daughter of Turkish immigrants and had therefore, in the eyes of the authorities, scarcely any human rights at all. Otto, fearful for a time that he might be caught, eventually realized that he had acted out his murderous fantasy on a relatively safe target. He began to relax, and as he relaxed he thought again about the intense compounding of pleasure it was to kill a girl as he had sex with her.

A year later, while he was working as a delivery boy for a jobbing printer, he picked up another Turkish girl in a café. An hour later she was dead, strangled with her pants just like the first girl.

'After that it became something he did,' the psychiatrist said. 'It was no longer something outside the normal run of events. He made it part of the bag of things that were his behaviour.'

When the tally of killings reached four the newspapers began to take notice. They ran speculative stories about a phantom Turk-hater who was taking his hatred out on the immigrants' women in an effort to drive them back to their own country. He even attracted a following among right-wing thugs, and there were two copycat murder attempts on Turkish women, both botched, one of them resulting in the attacker suffering serious genital damage from a spiked finger-ring worn by his victim for purposes of self-defence.

The fifth and sixth murders went so smoothly Otto almost believed he had dreamt them, but when he closed in on his seventh intended victim he walked into a trap. She was a police decoy, an officer trained in hand-to-hand combat who had spent a month hanging about the area where the other women had died, 'boiling for the chance to get him', as she put it. And she did get him. At the crucial moment she turned on Otto so savagely that she broke two of his ribs and dislocated his shoulder.

Otto was found to be entirely sane, although a year after starting his life sentence he was transferred to a psychiatric hospital because he showed signs of paranoid schizophrenia. He has remained in the psychiatric facility ever since.

Case 7

Five-year-old Peter was orphaned when both his parents were involved in a boating accident and drowned in Lake Michigan. After some deliberation by social services officials, Peter was put in the care of his grandmother at Evanston. She was an outwardly respectable widow who was, nevertheless, a secret drinker and chronically violent. She beat the boy for most misdemeanours, large or small. She also taught him to practise cunnilingus on her. At the age of eight Peter was taken into the care of a social services unit when the grandmother burned herself to death, smoking in bed following a heavy drinking bout. While he was in care, Peter was twice sodomized by social workers.

In 1981, when he was 25, Peter committed his first ever crime when he pulled up in his car on Lake Shore Drive in Chicago and flashed false police ID to a young woman standing alone at a corner. He told her she was to get in the car at once, and admitted later he was amazed when she did as she was told.

'When she was in the back seat I told her she was being arrested on suspicion of prostitution and I told her to put her hands on the back of my seat. She was really shaking and she was ready to do just anything I said. I put the handcuffs on her and told her to sit back.'

Peter drove to an underground car park several blocks away, parked the car in an isolated corner, then got into the back seat with the girl. He put a handkerchief in her mouth to stop her making a noise, then he raped her. When he had finished he got out his penknife and began cutting the girl on the thighs and arms, and when, in her pain and distress, she began choking on the handkerchief, he raped her again. Then he killed her by stabbing her through both eyes.

Late that night he threw the body on to the edge of a landfill site and it was not found for several days. By that time it had been bloated by the hot weather and attacked by seagulls and rats. It was proving very hard to identify the girl, and the means by which she had died, the papers suggested, would be impossible to determine.

Peter carried on with his job as a TV studio scenery-shifter by day and part-time aerobics instructor in the evenings. It was easy, he said, to make himself believe somebody else had killed the girl, or that he had just dreamt the events of that evening. Even when he did admit to himself that he had been the one who really and truly raped, tortured and murdered her, he saw it as an aberration, a glitch in an otherwise stable and more or less fulfilling life pattern.

He killed his second victim six weeks after the first, and this time he used a spike to put out her eyes and puncture her brain. The powerful feature of the killings, from Peter's point of view, was that his usual impotence left him completely. For those several minutes in the back of the car, he was as sexually potent as he could ever imagine being.

From then on he only had to think of the surge of potency he experienced when he attacked a victim, and he wanted to do it again. Only a few days separated the deaths of the second and third victims. The second body had not been found when the third woman was killed, and when Peter took the third body to the same place to dump it, he found that the second had practically rotted away in the summer heat.

'Maybe it was the feeling I got, that they were just disappearing after I killed them, that made me feel real easy about what I was doing,' he told a prison psychiatrist. 'Maybe it made me careless, too.'

Peter was caught by a police patrol as he was in the act of blinding his fourth victim, who nevertheless died before she reached hospital. At trial he was pronounced sane and was eventually sentenced to life imprisonment.

Care has to be exercised when trying to draw conclusions from small samples, but the foregoing cases have each been described as 'typical' by practitioners in the fields of criminology and forensic psychiatry. Particular tendencies and emphases in the lives of multiple-victim killers impress themselves on the people who have to work with them and with the particulars of their crimes.

'Bells ring at the mention of details which you perhaps didn't think were significant even a month ago,' says one analyst, 'and you realize, over and over, that there are patterns to these people, that they do have a kind of complex underlying

blueprint, and the longer you spend around them, the more likely it is you'll be able to identify its presence and its key elements.'

The possibilities for preventive work in this field have so far been only sketchily addressed. Currently there are no plans to embark on a large-scale classification of this category of murder, although many authorities believe that such a record, adequately monitored and maintained, would pay big dividends in future years.
'Especially when we bear in mind,' a psychiatrist says, *'that this kind of crime is on the upswing.'*

Although the murder of Sherry Long was now clearly linked to two previous murders, there was still not enough evidence to support any active line of inquiry. All the police had, apart from the bras used to kill the victims, was a tiny semen sample from one of the women, and that hadn't necessarily come from the killer. The sample was being analysed, but even if it could in some way be shown to have come from the man who committed the murder, it would not be much to go on. Physical evidence in the form of saliva, semen and blood is useless until the police have a suspect to compare it with. It can do no more, at best, than respond to scientific attempts at classification; it cannot put a name to the person it came from.

The detectives did what they could: they compiled a record of Sherry Long's last known movements, then waited for another murder to happen. But time passed and the next expected killing didn't take place. Ron Lancaster was prepared to bet that the killer had been arrested on another charge and was in jail. If that was the case, there would be very little chance of identifying him.

A national DNA database, of course, would change things dramatically. In the view of many people, such a facility would be a priceless asset in the war against crime, and would merit whatever budget might be necessary to set it up and keep it running. Like fingerprints, the DNA profiles of millions of people would be on record, ready to provide a match whenever a criminal slipped back into his old ways. In Britain there is a move towards legislation which would empower the police to take DNA profiles from convicted criminals and keep them on file, with a view to developing a national database. There have been calls for similar arrangements to be set up in the USA.

DNA fingerprinting (or DNA profiling as scientists now prefer to call it) virtually exploded on the scene in 1988, when it was hailed as the ultimate identity test. Dr (now Professor) Alec Jeffries, a geneticist at Leicester University, developed the test in 1984. He based the development on an idea he had while he was searching for genetic variations that would act as markers for inherited diseases. It occurred to him to ask himself why biochemical techniques for visualizing variations in DNA could not also be used to determine identity.

DNA profiling was first used in a forensic context in 1987, in the case of Colin Pitchfork, who was eventually found guilty of raping and strangling two 15-year-old girls in Leicester. When the hunt for the killer appeared to be going nowhere, the police organized DNA profiling tests for more than 5000 men living in and around a village close to the scenes of both crimes. Pitchfork tried to thwart the testing by getting a friend to stand in for him, but the story leaked out, Pitchfork was tested, and his DNA was found to match that of semen samples taken from the murdered girls.

The first American to be caught on the basis of DNA profiling was Tommy Lee Andrews. In 1988 he was given concurrent prison terms for sexual battery, armed burglary and aggravated battery. The same year Andrews was sentenced, a further seven rape and murder trials in the USA ended in convictions based on DNA profiling, and by the end of 1988 a further 100 suspects in criminal cases were being DNA tested prior to court proceedings.

DNA profiling depends for its success on being able to identify those sections of the DNA molecules in our body cells that vary from person to person. This highly variable DNA consists of

The Company of Strangers

segments that are repeated many times. Just how many times differs from one subject to another. To be used in analysis, DNA has to be extracted from a small sample of – for example – blood, semen, hair or skin. It is then cut into segments by restriction enzymes, which are proteins that split the DNA at exact points. The segments are then sorted by length in a gel through the action of electrophoresis (which is the movement of ultra microscopic particles in a fluid under the influence of an electric field). Segments containing sequences of repeated DNA are tagged with radioactive probes which allows the fragments to be visualized as a pattern of bands on a piece of light-sensitive film.

In the case of Tommy Lee Andrews, for example, the band patterns of his blood-cell DNA were a match, band for band, with the sperm found on the last victim. The patterns derived from the victim's blood samples, when compared to other people's blood sample films, were entirely different.

Some scientists estimated that the chances of another person having Andrews's DNA pattern were as high as one in 30 billion people. Expressed another way, the results meant that Andrews was the only man – beyond reasonable doubt – who could have left the sperm on the woman's body.

Many scientists, Alec Jeffries among them, believe that a national DNA database would be a good thing. In their view it would add immeasurably to the armoury of methods of detection, and would refine, considerably, the science of identification.

Others do not agree. Disputed profiles have been put forward as evidence in court cases, where the plates have been of such borderline clarity that only prejudice, one way or the other, could possibly underlie any 'determination'. There are also fears that because it takes an expert to interpret a plate, and because expert witnesses in criminal cases have sometimes shown themselves to be less than impartial, any number of innocent people could be convicted on the basis of what amounted to no more than an opinion – or worse, a bias.

'You can't hold up a DNA print and say, "Here it is, here's the *image that proves Joe Shmoe is the guilty party,"' says an attorney. 'Have you seen a DNA profile? It looks like nothing on earth. At least with a fingerprint, even though you still have to be told if it's a match or not, you can see something that has meaning. We all know what a fingerprint looks like, we know exactly what it relates to in the world of real things.*

'But the DNA plate - its groups of smudges in varying shades of grey and black. Sometimes they're so blurred the experts themselves don't accurately remember what they're supposed to prove. What I say is, get a system that gives nice clear results that somebody without a sixth sense can understand, then I'll be happy to get behind it in a court of law.'

There is also the undisputed possibility that the accused's DNA might turn out to be exactly like somebody else's. The chances of that happening are remote, but they are known to be a lot less remote than with fingerprinting. Twins, for example, have never been known to have matching fingerprints, but they do have identical DNA profiles.

The Institut für Rechtsmedizin in Berne, Switzerland, is possibly Europe's leading DNA laboratory. Manfred Hochmeister, who is in charge of the lab's DNA work, is well aware of the pros and cons of profiling. He believes databases are both inevitable and necessary, but there are still many technical issues to overcome. In addition, there have been many changes in the fundamental approaches to sampling and to the way in which results are produced. To embark on a database now, he says, would risk freezing development of DNA technology at an immature stage. Samples produced by an old method cannot be compared, at present, with samples derived using new procedures. The science and technology need time to `top out' before procedures are fixed into the patterns that would be necessary for day-in, day-out, large-scale profiling.

There are worries at the technicians' level, too. One man, whose job is to monitor samples used for DNA profiling and check on methods of collection, believes that there are just too many procedural areas where things can go wrong.

*'It's still too cranky to be used on anything like a routine basis,'
he says. 'Even at the present rate of productivity, things go
wrong all the time. Most mistakes don't happen in the profiling
process itself, they're mostly at the collection and preparation
stages.'*

People have to remember too much, he says, and often the
instructions are not clearly understood. Or if they are, there are
gross errors in the way they are carried out. Blood collection, for
example, is fraught with small difficulties; red cells have no nuclear
DNA in them, so enough blood has to be collected for DNA to be
extracted from the much scarcer white blood cells. Five millilitres
have to be drawn into what is known as an EDTA tube (the initials
stand for ethylenediaminetetraacetic acid), which extracts metallic
ions and not only prevents clotting, but inhibits enzymes and micro-
organisms, which can break down DNA during the storage period.

*'It's the exact opposite of the image that's grown up,' the
technician said, 'where you imagine this white-coated whiz
picking up bits of fluff, stray hairs, cigarette ends and a few other
bits and pieces, and then going into the lab with them to conjure
up a picture of the villain right down to his eye-colour and hat
size.'*

One lesson which is quickly learned by those working with
genetic material is that it corrupts very easily. Swabs taken from
vagina, rectum, mouth and other orifices have to be air-dried as
quickly as possible, and they must not be subjected to heat. They
then have to be stored in a deep freeze if there is a likelihood of any
delay in sending them to the laboratory. Liquid semen in a rape
case must be removed from the victim's body with a pipette, placed
in a small test tube and frozen solid as fast as possible if there is to
be any hope of obtaining usable DNA material at the laboratory.

*'Hairs are another area where the mythology is hard to fight
against,' the technician says. 'The usual notion is that if you find*

a hair, you're on to the blueprint of somebody. That's not quite true. Hairs, whether they come from the head, the pubis, the armpits or the eyebrows, are no use for profiling unless there are a sufficient number of root or follicle cells attached to them. The shaft of the hair isn't any use, you see. If a hair has fallen out, or if it's come out on a comb, the chances are it's a moulting hair and there's precious little root material. They have to be plucked to be any good.

'Even when there's a whole bodily organ to collect samples from, you have to be properly selective,' the technician says. 'A couple of grams or so of the organ have to be taken, and the material's got to come from what's called the parenchyma of the organ, that's the functioning bit rather than the framework. The tissue has to be put in a little plastic tube with no fixative or preservative, and this, as you would guess by now, has to be frozen solid.'

Probably the best organ for DNA recovery is the spleen, although muscle, kidney and liver can also be used. At one time the material had to be absolutely fresh and collected as soon after death as possible, but in recent times new techniques have permitted the recovery of usable DNA from old material. Professor Alec Jeffries confirmed the identity of a young woman who had lain buried in a garden for eight years, and whose body was reduced to a skeleton. To effect the identification he used dried bone-marrow extracted from the skeleton by the eminent Home Office pathologist, Professor Bernard Knight.

'It's the same with any new procedure that keeps on changing its features as it develops,' says the technician. 'At present people haven't quite found a footing. New simplified techniques will come along, though. As far as I'm concerned, they can't get here soon enough.'

A great hope for the future of DNA profiling is the technique known as polymerase chain reaction (PCR). DNA polymerase creates the phosphate bonds between the sugars in the 'backbone' of the DNA double helix. In the PCR technique, DNA is chemically encouraged by the polymerase to replicate itself; the result is that a small amount of genetic material turns into a larger amount. In practical terms this means that the DNA in a small sample – so small it can't be used for profiling – can be used to 'grow' enough of itself to make straightforward testing possible.

The PCR technique was used by Manfred Hochmeister at the Institut für Rechtsmedizin in 1994 to analyse the DNA of a single hair root. The hair had been found on the seat of a car used in the murder of a Czech prostitute; the hair belonged not to the murderer but to his victim. It was fortunate that the Czech police knew who had been driving the car. His name was Jack Unterweger. He had become famous in his native Germany when, serving a life sentence for murder, he began to write. His work had considerable commercial merit, and in a relatively short time Unterweger had published a book and several plays. His charisma began to grow alongside his fame and in 1990 he was released from prison much earlier than would normally have been expected, given the seriousness of his crime.

Shortly after Unterweger was released from prison, the dead bodies of several women were found in the woods around Vienna. Investigating the killings, the Viennese police soon realized that all of the women had been murdered by the same person. And there was more. From studies of the killer's *modus operandi* it gradually emerged that the Viennese killings were part of a larger pattern. In addition to these murders, several other women appeared to have been killed by the same person. Their bodies had been found in Czechoslovakia, Austria and Switzerland.

One of Austria's leading investigators, Ernst Geiger, was put in charge of the investigation of the local murders. He was still co-ordinating the various strands of the cases when a retired German policeman read about the killings in his newspaper and recognized striking similarities between these murders and one he had investigated in 1974. It had been the murder to which Jack Unterweger had confessed, and for which he was sentenced to life imprisonment.

So Ernst Geiger's inquiries suddenly attained a precise point of focus. The first day's research into Unterweger's movements produced the fact that, while working under contract as a celebrity journalist, he had interviewed the chief of the Viennese police about the spate of local murders. Further research showed that right across Europe, wherever one of the murders had occurred, Unterweger had been there in the guise of an investigative journalist. Astonishingly, eyewitness evidence even put him publicly in the company of several of the dead women.

The DNA evidence of the hair from the Czech prostitute was enough to raise a warrant to search Unterweger's flat. There the police found a menu from a fish restaurant in Malibu, California. There were also photographs of Unterweger posing with female members of the LAPD. Ernst Geiger wasted no time letting the LA police know about the investigation he was conducting, and advising them that his suspect had apparently spent some time in Los Angeles.

Officers of the LAPD homicide division established that Jack Unterweger had spent almost a month in LA, ostensibly writing an article about prostitution for an upmarket German magazine. The police department had even given him a guided tour of the various red-light districts. During that time, although Unterweger had introductions to some prestigious levels of Beverly Hills society, he stayed in fairly seedy hotels, a number of them frequented by hookers.

The first two strangling victims (the murders investigated by homicide detective Jim Harper), had last been seen alive a few yards from the Hotel Cecil, where Jack Unterweger had been living at that particular time. Sherry Long, the woman found dead on the day of the partial eclipse, had worked the streets around the Hollywood 8 motel, where Unterweger had recently moved and where he was registered the night Sherry died. He became prime suspect in the killings of the three women who had been strangled with their bras and dumped on open ground.

The European and American murders, 11 in all, shared numerous features, but the strength of an eventual case would depend on the police being able to demonstrate that the similarities were unusual enough to emanate from one source and one alone. To strengthen the case against Unterweger, the Austrian police contacted the FBI, with a view to using the extensive comparison facilities available in the Violent Criminal Apprehension Program (VICAP) database. The FBI agreed to co-operate.

VICAP, the brainchild of Pierce R. Brooks, is a computerized data centre designed to gather, organize and analyse detailed information on specific crimes of violence. It will accept criminal data which meet the following criteria:

A: Solved or unsolved murders or attempted murders, with emphasis on cases which involve an abduction; cases which appear random, motiveless or sexual in orientation; cases which are, or are suspected to be, parts of a series.
B: Missing persons, where the circumstances of the case strongly suggest foul play, and the victim has not yet been found.
C: Dead bodies, unidentified, where death is known to be, or suspected to be, the result of homicide.

Cases where the offender has been identified or arrested are still submitted, so that unsolved cases held in the VICAP system can be assessed for possible connection with known offenders. The scope of VICAP will soon be expanded to include rape, child sexual abuse and cases of arson.

Any links between case-related information from police sources, and the cases held in the VICAP system, are quickly established. Comparisons are made on the basis of MO, victimology, physical evidence, description of suspect, and reported behaviour before, during and after the crime.

When the Austrian police asked for assistance in the Unterweger case, VICAP held details of over 4000 stranger-murders committed in the USA. Agent Greg McCrary fed in the details of the European murders and found only four matches, three of them the Los Angeles 'bra murders' which criminalist Lynn Herrold had linked the year before.

At the eventual trial in Graz, Austria, statistical arguments were crucial in convincing the jury that this hideous series of murders was the work of one man. In 600 days of liberty following his 'life' sentence for murder, the court was told, Unterweger had taken the lives of 11 women. The killings were acts of heartless, sadistic slaughter committed by a man with no regard for the sanctity of human life. In the end, Unterweger was found guilty of nine murders, including the three in Los Angeles.

The case illustrates the strengths and the weaknesses of forensic science. Once Unterweger was in the courtroom, a few scraps of incriminating scientific evidence were vital to the prosecutor's case. But it was not forensic science, for all its efforts and cunning, that put Unterweger in the court in front of a judge. Old-fashioned police work did that.

FBI Agent Greg McCrary says the future of science in fighting crime may lie less in developing new methods of detecting and using physical evidence, than in helping police use the data they obtain, through conventional police work, in a more scientific manner.

A few hours after the guilty verdict was handed down by the jury, Jack Unterweger strangled himself in his cell with a garrotte fashioned from the drawstring of his tracksuit pants. Lynn Herrold later examined the knot with great interest.

bad

In 1979 Roger Leroy Degarmo was tried for the murder of Kimberley Anne Strickler which took place at a remote spot 40 miles southwest of Houston, Texas. 'She was kidnapped,' said a police spokesman, 'and driven out to Fort Bend County. There she was shot in the back of the head in the trunk of her own car.'

The police built a strong case against Degarmo. They had the murder weapon as well as conclusive fingerprint evidence. And they even had an eyewitness:

'I was driving along Allfield Road when a gentleman stepped out of a car and flagged me down,' said John Moers, a construction foreman. 'They were up there on the levee [embankment], stuck. He asked me if I'd push him out. I pushed him out, then his female companion pulled a gun on me and everything started from there on.'

The man who had flagged him down – Roger Degarmo – got behind the wheel in John Moers' truck and told his girlfriend to drive the car.

John Moers continued, 'They went down the Allfield road and made a right, then we went down to some oil tanks and he pulled over. He waved to the girl to pull over too.'

At this point Moers realized Degarmo had a girl in the boot of his car. Degarmo said that he was going to retie her hands.

'He went back and opened up the trunk and they told me to get down on the floorboards of the truck and the girlfriend held a gun on me.'

Moers did not see the girl in the car, because of his position in his truck, but he could see the side of Degarmo's car, and he heard everything clearly, as he explained:

'He went back to the trunk and told Strickler to stand up, he was going to retie her hands. She stood up and he told her to turn around, and she said something like "I won't rat on you, I won't squeal on you", and then boom! He shot her, out there. She fell back down in the trunk and he closed the lid.'

John Moers eventually managed to escape from Degarmo by leaping out of his moving truck. Some time later Degarmo and his companion were arrested.

After a heavily-publicized trial Degarmo was found guilty of first-degree murder and was sentenced to death by lethal injection. Nowadays, however, strong physical evidence in a murder case is not always enough to secure a verdict that will stick. On the day Degarmo's death sentence was to be carried out, a judge in Houston granted a stay of execution which meant that Degarmo would remain on Death Row until a review of his case was completed.

'To me it's reliving the whole thing again,' said Kimberley Strickler's mother. 'He did it, so why a stay? I don't understand.'

Degarmo's new attorney, Greg Gladden, announced he had fresh evidence which would show the defendant had a brain disorder which was never mentioned in evidence by his previous lawyers.

'The jury needs to understand Roger Degarmo and where he's come from,' Gladden said. 'Then they'll make a decision as to what level of responsibility he should take for any actions taken by him.'

In 1993 Roger Degarmo was tried a second time and the latest clinical technology was used to help evaluate his state of mind at the time he committed his crime. The well established facts of the case had to make room for new claims about Degarmo's state of mind and his general level of sanity back in 1979. After hearing expert testimony from both sides, the jury was asked to make a crucial decision: could the accused be held responsible for the death of Kimberley Anne Strickler, or had his reason diminished to such an extent that he could not exercise civilized judgement? In short, was he mad or was he bad?

Nigel Walker, Emeritus Professor of Criminology at Cambridge University, has spent 30 years studying the relationship between crime and insanity. He explained that there are records to show that insanity was recognized by the law centuries before medical psychiatry came into existence – in fact insanity is a legal concept rather than a medical one. English criminal law defines insanity as a defect of reason, arising from mental disease, that is severe enough to prevent a defendant from knowing what he did, or that what he did was wrong.

'The insanity defence can be traced back to Roman times,' Walker said. 'There was a Roman provincial governor in the third century AD who pardoned a homicide because, he said, "a madman is punished enough by his madness".'

In the thirteenth century plea rolls were introduced into the English legal system. These were detailed records of proceedings in legal cases, the forerunners of present-day transcripts, and they serve as clear illustrations of how the law was administered in the late Middle Ages. Nigel Walker cited the example of a plea roll concerning an insane homicide.

'It tells us that Richard of Cheddeston was known to be crazy because he tried to throw himself into a pond and his wife dragged him out. They went home and some time later he strangled both his children, then his wife when she came home and found them. Well he was known to be crazy so the Sheriff simply put him in jail and then, as was usual by that time, consulted the King who could give instructions about his disposal. Six years later the King actually ordered an enquiry of a kind that would nowadays be called a mental health review tribunal, to decide whether Richard was safe to be released.'

The local view was that Richard was not safe. He appeared well enough, but because it was a hot summer the authorities were not keen to run the risk of having a known crazy man at large in conditions that could induce a relapse. What finally happened to Richard of Cheddeston we do not know, because the roll ends there.

Today, a jury might find a person like Richard not guilty by reason of insanity, a concept which is embodied in the McNaughton Rules. It is interesting to look at the original case which gave the Rules their name, and an historically related case which preceded it by three years.

In 1840 Edward Oxford fired two pistols at Queen Victoria's coach as she travelled past him on Constitution Hill. At the time of the offence Oxford was 18 and he obviously knew what he had done; that much was enough to get him hanged under the law as it then stood. But at his trial there was considerable public sympathy because he was so young, and because he did not appear to be entirely in his right mind.

Witnesses came forward to talk about the odd behaviour of older members of Oxford's family, demonstrating that there was a known familial history of mental instability. Dr Thomas Hodgkin (for whom Hodgkin's disease was named) testified that Edward Oxford was suffering from 'a lesion of the will'. It was a bizarre diagnosis, but nobody challenged it. Dr John Connolly, another prominent physician who specialized in treating mental illness, attributed Oxford's behaviour to his oddly-shaped forehead and a resulting malformation of the front of his brain which, he said, could give rise to a variety of mental disorders. (Under some aggressive questioning by the prosecution, Dr Connolly did admit he knew people with skulls much the same shape who suffered from no mental aberrations or even marginally odd behaviour.)

In his summing up the judge, Chief Justice Denman, emphasized his belief that any person who committed an offence while under the control of an irresistible illness should be acquitted of blame. The jury, swayed by the evidence of lofty medical witnesses, and by the judge's pointed summation, eventually returned a verdict of 'guilty but insane'. Oxford was committed to Bethlem hospital where, according to the warden's journal, any evidence of insanity quickly disappeared.

Three years later, on 20 January 1843, 29-year-old Daniel McNaughton, the son of a Glasgow wood-turner, shot and killed Edward Drummond, Private Secretary to Sir Robert Peel, the Prime Minister. McNaughton committed the murder in broad daylight in front of several witnesses, and freely admitted he had mistaken Drummond for the Prime Minister.

At McNaughton's trial, evidence was heard from several witnesses, among them his father, the Provost of Glasgow and the Commissioner of Police for Glasgow. Their evidence showed that for years the defendant had been under the impression that a number of people were conspiring against him. He had talked about being harassed by spies who had been recruited by Catholic priests, with the help of the Jesuits and the Tories. For more than a year before the shooting the Commissioner of Police had known about McNaughton's condition, which nowadays would have been diagnosed as paranoid schizophrenia.

During the trial McNaughton said, 'I was driven to desperation by persecution.' This admission showed that although he suffered delusions, he knew what he was doing and he knew, also, that killing Drummond was a crime.

Acting for the defence, Dr Edward Thomas Monro, a specialist with 30 years' experience of dealing with insane patients, said, 'I consider the act of killing Mr Drummond to have been committed under a delusion. The act itself I look upon as the crowning act of the whole matter... as a carrying out of the pre-existing idea which had haunted him for years.'

Several other doctors who were called to give evidence agreed that McNaughton was insane. The prosecution case was destroyed finally when two doctors appearing for the Crown (one of whom, Dr Forbes Winslow, had not examined McNaughton but had only been a spectator at the trial) agreed completely with the doctors appearing for the defence: McNaughton, they declared, was certainly insane. The jury did not even retire and the foreman read the verdict to a hushed courtroom: 'We find the prisoner not guilty on the grounds of insanity.'

The outcome of Daniel McNaughton's trial was received quite differently from that of Edward Oxford. A storm of protest raged across the country. The leniency of a court towards one deranged soul was a charitable event, but it was also an exceptional event; the establishment and its press, it seemed, did not like to witness the beginning of what looked uncomfortably like a trend. Queen Victoria herself felt so strongly that she wrote to Sir Robert Peel:

We have seen the trials of Oxford and McNaughton conducted by the ablest lawyers of the day, and they allow the jury to pronounce the verdict of Not Guilty on Account of Insanity when everybody is morally convinced that both malefactors were perfectly conscious and aware of what they did....

The government could not ignore the pressure of discontent, subjective and unreasoning though it was. At a debate in the House of Lords the Lord Chancellor, Lord Lyndhurst, proposed they restore an old piece of constitutional procedure whereby the House gained the opinions of learned judges on points of law by asking them questions on particular topics. Parliament agreed to the suggestion and the Lord Chancellor asked a panel of senior judges five questions designed to clarify the legal position on delusional insanity.

The judges' answers, given on 19 June 1893, were the basis of the so-called McNaughton Rules. The answers were delivered with the qualification, 'Assuming your Lordships' inquiries are confined to those persons who labour under such partial delusions only, and are not in other respects insane.'

The following is an abridgement of the main points of the McNaughton Rules.

1 Every man is to be presumed sane and to possess a sufficient degree of reason to be responsible for his crimes, until the opposite is proved.

2 An insane person is punishable according to the nature of the crime committed, if he knew, at the time of committing the crime, that he was acting contrary to the law of the land.

3 To establish a defence on the ground of insanity, it must be clearly proved that at the time of the act, the accused was labouring under such delusion as not to know the nature and quality of the act he was committing, or, if he did know, that he did not know he was doing wrong.

4 The insane person must bear the same responsibility that he would if his delusion were real. For example, if he is under the deluded belief that another man is going to kill him, and he then kills that man in what he believes to be self-defence, he would

be exempt from punishment. If his delusion told him, on the other hand, that the other man had slandered him, or had stolen his property, and he went ahead and killed the man, then he would be liable to punishment.

5 It is the jury's role to decide, in the end, whether or not a defendant is insane.

The rules put emphasis on the importance of the accused understanding the concepts of right and wrong, and on there being a necessary link between the content of the delusion and the crime. These guidelines were framed to appease an angry public (and its monarchy) and they were certainly more stringent than the guidelines that previously existed. If the 'right-wrong test' had been applied at the time of McNaughton's own trial, there would have been no chance of a not-guilty verdict.

The McNaughton Rules have no statutory basis, but they are accepted by the courts as having equal status with statutory law. They have been heavily criticized for presenting a concept of insanity that is far too narrow – e.g. critics of the Rules have pointed out that insanity affects not only the cognitive faculties, but also the emotions and the will.

'The McNaughton Rules provide no middle ground between a complete excuse or being found completely guilty,' said Nigel Walker. 'So, England copied the Scots' notion of diminished responsibility, and put it into the Homicide Act of 1957.'

The relevant passage is in section 2 of the Act:

Where a person kills or is party to the killing of another, he shall not be convicted of murder if he was suffering from such abnormality of mind (whether arising from a condition of arrested or retarded development of mind or any inherent causes or induced by disease or injury) as substantially impaired his mental responsibility for his

acts and omissions in doing or being party to the killing.

In practice, a person charged with murder can plead that he is not guilty of murder, but is guilty of manslaughter on the grounds of diminished responsibility. If the defence is acceptable to the judge and the prosecuting authority, no trial takes place and a sentence for manslaughter is passed. If the judge or the prosecution do not find the defence acceptable, then the case goes to trial. The jury then has to decide, from the medical evidence, whether the accused was suffering from abnormality of mind at the time the crime was committed, and whether the abnormality was severe enough to impair his responsibility. If the defendant is found guilty of manslaughter, then the judge can impose whatever sentence he thinks is deserved – and that can include life imprisonment – on the grounds of dangerousness. For a conviction of murder, on the other hand, there is a statutory conviction of life imprisonment.

'We already had a defence of provocation to murder,' Professor Walker said, 'which would downgrade murder to manslaughter, and what the lawyers did was to provide that an alternative defence to provocation could be diminished responsibility – abnormality of mind, from whatever cause, sufficient to give you a partial excuse for what you did. Nowadays, very few homicide defendants plead insanity. They usually plead diminished responsibility.'

In the case examined here, details have been changed to prevent distress or embarrassment to innocent people. The case, nevertheless, is a real one, involving a man called Sammy, aged 26, who was accused of sexually assaulting and murdering an elderly woman after she surprised him in the act of burgling her home.

Before Sammy's case went to court there was a case conference, where his lawyers and psychiatrists met to decide the best way to present a defence to the jury. Those present were Lucy, the solicitor who represented Sammy legally and who had arranged previously for him to be interviewed by the two psychiatrists present at the meeting; Stephen, Sammy's barrister, who would have to argue the case in court and John and David, both experienced psychiatrists who had each spent considerable time interviewing Sammy.

'Let's look at the options and see what might happen to him,' suggested Lucy. *'If he pleads guilty, or if he is found guilty of murder, then he gets life imprisonment, no option. Then he could be transferred later to a psychiatric hospital for treatment. If he gets found guilty of manslaughter, then he could get an interim hospital order, to see if he's treatable.'*

'Lucy and I have discussed the psychiatric angle in this case,' said Stephen, the barrister, *'and whether or not a defence of diminished responsibility is workable, particularly in the light of the prosecution expert's report. Although he says that our client has a personality disorder, he says it doesn't go far enough to amount to diminished responsibility.'*

The refusal of the prosecution to accept that the defendant has a significant defect of mind was a serious obstacle for the defence, but there was more in this instance.

'Not only has he had sex with an old woman, in her own home and against her will,' Stephen said, *'but he's got a shoe fetish. He's going to be seen from the outset as a weirdo.'*

Would it help, he asked the psychiatrists, to use that angle – Sammy's distinct oddity as a human being – as the basis for a psychiatric defence?

'The first thing to establish,' John said, *'is whether or not there is an abnormality of mind. In this individual we have a lifelong history of behavioural abnormality. He had problems as a child which have lasted throughout his life.'*

In the course of questioning by David, Sammy revealed that when he was a boy, in addition to imagining naked women when he masturbated, he also fantasized about women's shoes, and the fetish persisted into adult life; 'They just turn me on, you know? The feel of the shoes...'. He had also entertained notions of killing himself.

'I think this is a case where the patient has never matured in important aspects of himself and his sexual development.' said David. 'The psychiatric diagnosis isn't one where there is much dispute. Other doctors would agree that he suffers from a personality disorder.'

John explained that like many people with personality disorders, Sammy had developed a depressive illness. Rather more unusually he also had a fetish – the psychiatric term for this and other sexual aberrations is a paraphilia – and in John's view the combination of disturbances had led Sammy to commit a homicide in the context of a burglary.

Sammy told David that when he entered the old woman's bedroom he did not ransack it, he simply looked around.

'I was just touching things, picking them up. She had this like, powder-puff thing, and I remember picking it up and smelling it. Then she must have heard me, because she came into the room. I couldn't believe that she was in there, I was so sure there was no one in that house.'

He explained that when he attacked the old woman, it began as an act of resistance. She was shouting at him, berating him for being in her home. 'I just wanted her out of my face, she was in my face, you know? Telling me off.'

He pushed the woman and she fell on the bed. 'And then I got excited.' His excitement was sexual, he said. The violence – he put his hand over the woman's mouth to silence her and then suffocated her – came after the sexual assault, when he panicked, realizing what he had done.

Sammy's halting recollection of previous events and emotions highlighted a weakness in the legal guidelines. Nigel Walker has said that the McNaughton Rules give a psychiatrist an enormously difficult job.

'You're talking to a man in his cell, or in his hospital ward, weeks or months after his crime, trying to find out from what he says exactly what went through his mind at the time of the crime. Not only is that difficult, but it's unreliable. The man may be under sedation at the time you see him, he may have had legal advice about what he should or should not say to the psychiatrist, he may have a confused memory. It may be like trying to find out from somebody what they dreamt about last night.'

According to the psychiatrist called David, Sammy was accurate in his statement that killing the old woman was an accident, and that he had never had any intention to kill anybody.

'My view,' said John, the other psychiatrist, 'is that he demonstrates evidence of compulsion. In the literature there is a clear link between people who display fetishes and the development of violent sexual behaviour.'

'But I didn't hear anything that said the physical assault followed on from the sexual assault,' commented Lucy. 'I thought they were separate....'

John said, 'I don't think they were. His explanation of that has to be very suspect.'

'We both agree this guy has got a serious problem of personality development,' said David, 'but as far as I'm concerned, it demonstrates only that he is strange, he is unusual, he's not like ordinary people. I don't see his condition as directly linked to the act in the way John does.'

'If you're going to rely on a defence of diminished responsibility, Stephen, the barrister, pointed out, *'you've got to show that the act itself, which caused the death, is connected to the personality disorder.'*

'That's why,' said David, 'John's view supports a diminished responsibility defence better than mine. I would say the link is because of his personality he ends up in this screwy situation and he panics. So in a way I see it as a panic reaction, something any immature person might do when things happen unexpectedly.'

Lucy asked David if Sammy's immaturity was part of his personality disorder.

'It is, there is a link, it's just not a very strong or direct one. We're talking about an adversarial system here,' he added regretfully, 'about what will work with a jury.'

John agreed that David's was the weaker argument. 'On the other hand I don't think there's an awful lot of difference between what David's saying and what I'm saying. I'm perhaps drawing a stronger link between the sexual behaviour and the actual act of putting the hand over the mouth.'

Both defence psychiatrists agreed that Sammy had a severe personality disorder. But the law required them to do more than make a medical diagnosis. They would have to explain to the court what was going through Sammy's head as he suffocated his victim, and here David and John had divergent opinions. Although from a medical point of view they were saying much the same thing, the degree of difference between them was absolutely vital. If, as David believed and Sammy insisted, the killing was an accident, diminished responsibility as a defence was not going to work. An alternative defence would be to plead manslaughter, on the grounds of lack of intent to kill.

'I have to decide,' Stephen told the psychiatrists, 'whether either of you sound convincing enough on this question to be able to call you as witnesses. At the moment I'm afraid I'm not convinced by either of you.'

'If you go for a manslaughter verdict,' David said, 'based on lack of intent to murder, then obviously I could say a lot about the mitigating elements and so on.'

Stephen didn't seem any more convinced. 'There are two possible decisions here,' he said. 'One is we run a manslaughter defence, straightforward, without bringing in any psychiatric evidence, as opposed to the psychiatric defence which explains his whole history, his state of mind, as far back as you can go.'

'Either way,' said Lucy, 'you're going to have to put in the psychiatric evidence, even if you're not running diminished responsibility, because even if you're going for straightforward lack of intent, you've still got to explain his weirdness.'

'Well, you'd have to argue that it's admissible,' Stephen said. 'Nowadays it's harder to get in that kind of evidence without a specific end in sight.'

'As a point of principle,' said David, 'speaking as a forensic psychiatrist, I believe very strongly that cases like this ought to come under diminished responsibility. To me, it's absolutely straightforward. This guy has got a severe personality disorder, and the only issue legally, which would be fair to argue about, is the extent to which there is a causal connection between the disorder and the act.'

Whatever happened, Stephen said, they couldn't afford to fudge the decision. 'I think we all agree, this isn't the strongest case of diminished responsibility, and we can't call our client to the stand. He'd tie himself up in knots. He'd effectively say anything under skilful cross-examination, and we really need to call the psychiatric evidence to get him some sympathy. It's the only way, really, of giving the case a human face, instead of the jury seeing him as a monster standing in the dock.'

Lucy told the others that now she had heard what they'd had to say, and had the psychiatric reports, she would visit Sammy and go through all the various alternatives with him:

'Guilty to murder, that's one possibility, not guilty of murder but guilty of manslaughter because of lack of intent – that's a not-very-strong case; and not guilty of murder but guilty of manslaughter by reason of diminished responsibility, by reason of mental disorder. I'll let you know what he decides he would like to go for.'

In the real case on which the reconstruction was based, Sammy stuck to his story that the killing was an accident. In spite of the fact that all the psychiatrists who examined him agreed that he had a personality disorder, not one of them was called to give evidence. The jury eventually found Sammy guilty, which meant he went to prison instead of a secure hospital like Broadmoor or Rampton.

For Roger Degarmo in Texas, the stakes were much higher than they had been for Sammy. If the verdict at the re-trial went against him, he would die. As matters stood, a public re-telling of the facts in the case was not going to help his chances.

'Kimberley was 20 years old, attractive, described as vivacious,' said Sid Crowley, state prosecutor. *'I gathered, just talking to her parents and other people that knew her, that she was a person that liked to help others. In fact one of the neighbours at the apartment complex where she lived was an elderly man and he told police that from time to time she would bake cakes for him and his wife.'*

'I went to see him in 1985 and talked to him for about two, two-and-a-half hours,' said defence attorney Greg Gladden. *'He probably did most of the talking, but I was really aggressive, trying to get him to let me represent him – not because I liked*

him, or because his life was worth saving, but because I didn't
believe that my tax money and my state government should be
in the business of killing citizens.'

On the day of the crime Kimberley was having time off from her
job as a medical technician in a blood bank. At some time mid-
morning she had gone to visit her father, who lived in another part
of Houston, and she had left there about 3.30 p.m. Kimberley was
last seen leaving a grocery store about four blocks from her
apartment at about 4.00 or 4.30 p.m.

'One of the grocery checkout clerks remembered her,' said
Crowley, 'and a receipt was later found in her car. Roger
Degarmo and his female accomplice Helen Mahayer lived in an
apartment complex about four blocks from the grocery store,
and Degarmo wanted to steal a car to use in a robbery. So he
and Helen Mahayer walked over to the parking lot and according
to her 1980 testimony, Roger was planning to get an elderly
person, or some other person it would be easy to take a car
from. Kimberley came out of the grocery store, and Degarmo
asked if she could give them a ride to their apartment because it
was cold. She said, "Sure, hop on in, I can give you a ride". They
both got in the car and after they had driven out of the parking
lot Degarmo pulled a pistol and told Kimberley to drive to an
underground parking garage several blocks away.'

At the underground car park Degarmo made Kimberley get out
of the car. He walked her round to the back, opened the boot, tied
her up, forced her into the boot and closed it. She remained locked
in there until the car was eventually parked by the petrol tanks off
the Allfield Road and then, as described by John Moers, Degarmo
opened the boot and shot Kimberley dead.

Studying the papers in the Degarmo case, Gladden soon
uncovered procedural problems with the 1979 conviction, including
the fact that the previous lawyers had failed to introduce medical
testimony about the defendant's previous head injury. Using this

omission as a central argument for a re-evaluation of the case, Gladden managed to put together a dossier strong enough to get his client a second trial. Even so, he knew the outcome could easily be the same as first time, since the prosecution still had the eyewitness testimony of John Moers. To counter that evidence Gladden was going to have to come up with something very persuasive.

'The first time I met with Roger,' Gladden said, 'some fairly recent research had come out about the disproportionate number of people on Death Row in the United States that had suffered head injuries, and I do remember discussing it with Roger and him kind of lighting up and saying, "Well, I had a head injury".'

When Degarmo was 19 a large truck tyre he was working on blew up in his face. The steel hoop securing the inner rim of the tyre to the hub flew out at high sped and struck him in the face.

'It almost took the top of his head off,' Gladden said. 'It impacted Roger at the nose and right cheek. It severed the cartilage of his nose, completely demolished the bone under his eye and literally almost took off the right front part of his face.'

Gladden realized that if he could show this injury had caused severe and permanent brain damage, he might have the nucleus of a plausible defence.

'At the time of the killing,' he said, 'Roger was suffering from brain damage and multiple drug problems. He was in a very stressful situation, there was the woman in the car screaming bloody murder, he was stuck in the mud – all of those things compound each other, so the fact that he would do something immoral was perfectly understandable.'

Degarmo had his own way of describing the event that put him on Death Row.

'The girl that I shot,' he said, 'was an object. She was not a girl. I was trying to create silence. This girl was screaming, I was in a

tight situation, the gun was pointing in her direction and I pulled the trigger. This is how that girl got killed.'

Gladden had his client examined by a neurologist. The results, he claimed, provided moderate evidence of an old head injury, but the same testing turned up a number of personality flaws that Gladden did not want to air in a courtroom.

'Things like future dangerousness and sexual weirdness, and some other problems that we really didn't want to talk about. The evidence was such a double-edged sword we decided we probably wouldn't use that neurologist.' What Gladden needed was a clearly worded, unequivocal diagnosis of mental damage: *'...Something that would pigeonhole Roger'.*

While Gladden was looking through professional textbooks for inspiration, a copy of Kaplan and Sadock's *Synopsis of Psychiatry* fell open at page 81, a colour plate, and right there was what he had been looking for.

'It was an image of a brain with a red spot on it. As soon as I saw it I realized this was what I wanted to show the jury. I wanted to show them a picture of Roger's brain with something like a red spot, an organic problem that had caused his personality disorder and which was obvious to all of us....'

So Gladden arranged for Degarmo to have PET scans made of his brain. PET (Positron Emission Tomography) is probably the most powerful tool available for examining the living human brain. It is a difficult and costly procedure that still needs to be administered by highly skilled technicians.

To obtain a scan, the operator injects a radioactively labelled substance, often sugar, directly into the patient's bloodstream. The solution soon circulates up into the brain. The patient is then placed carefully in a scanning device which, as Degarmo puts it, resembles a giant doughnut.

Since glucose is the brain's main fuel, the radioactive solution will tend to concentrate in the parts of the brain which are most active. Because the sugar is radioactive it emits positrons, which collide with surrounding electrons, and in colliding they emit gamma rays. The gamma rays' flashes are plotted by the scanning equipment and a computer translates the data into a brain image, colour-coded to help evaluation and diagnosis.

One of the world's most advanced centres for the study and development of PET scanning is at San Antonio in Texas. The interpretation of scans calls for a thorough understanding of brain function and the numerous implications of abnormal results. Dr Helen Mayberg is a neurologist and a leading PET scan scientist.

'My major field of interest is behavioural neurology. So as a research scientist I am interested in the relationship between brain structure, brain function, and behaviour. I've concentrated much of my professional life on the study of brain areas that regulate mood and emotion.'

Dr Mayberg explained how the brain pictures are presented for her to evaluate.

'It's much how you would slice a salami,' she said. 'The brain starts, really, about eye level, and one takes a series of images from low in the brain to high in the brain, in strict order, and one can then look at these pictures on a screen reconstruction by a computer. So we have fine, visible slices of the brain from low down around the level of the ears and then consecutively up to the top of the head.'

The PET scanner, Dr Mayberg said, is an extremely powerful research tool.

'Unlike an anatomical study, a CT scan or an MRI scan which give you only information about brain structure, a PET scan tells you about brain work, brain function – be it brain energy metabolism, be it brain blood flow, or even measures of certain biochemical substances in the brain and their particular locations.'

In well-controlled studies, Dr Mayberg added, the PET scan is of great value in identifying patterns of brain abnormality:

'Particularly in the evaluation of patients with epilepsy, brain tumours, dementia, and patients with abnormal movements like they have in Parkinson's disease. Studies have been done very carefully to look at well-characterized and well-defined illnesses to see if a pattern can be identified with these techniques, and for the illnesses I've talked about it's worked very well.'

Relating brain scans to behaviour, however, has proved difficult.

'Although behaviour work is very interesting and very challenging,' Dr Mayberg said, 'it is totally, totally in its infancy. There has been no substantive work whatsoever. Violent behaviour, criminal thinking, issues of responsibility or judgement, or lack of judgement, have never been evaluated by this technique. Quite frankly, I think it's really hard to figure out how one would design a study to evaluate judgement, or remorse, or insight, or impulsivity, because even different psychologists or clinicians will disagree on the definition of those behaviours.'

Nevertheless, Greg Gladden arranged for Roger Degarmo to be brain scanned. But getting pictures of Degarmo's brain was just a beginning. It was vitally important to Gladden that he enlist the right person to interpret the images for a jury. He found the man he wanted in Dallas, where Dr John Hickey runs a small diagnostic clinic associated with a well-known fitness centre.

'Most of the people who come here,' Dr Hickey explained, 'are sent by the companies that employ them. My primary organ of interest has been the heart. My partner Dr Simon has been more interested in brain imaging, dating back well over a decade. So I relied somewhat on his opinion because we hadn't done many of these here at the hospital.'

In Hickey's view, the scans of Degarmo's brain showed

abnormality, and his partner agreed with that.

'One area we needed to look at was the temporal lobes,' Dr Hickey said. 'They sit down in the temple regions. They run more or less from just behind the eyes back, and extend up at the sides. They are extremely important in terms of behaviour.'

Looking at scans of Degarmo's right temporal lobe, Dr Hickey said that the degree of asymmetry meant a significant reduction in brain function, probably in the order of 30 or 40 per cent of the functional level of the opposite side.

'That means this part of Roger's brain is not functioning normally.'

So Greg Gladden had his defence. In December 1992, for the second time, Roger Degarmo found himself on trial for his life. Prosecutor Sid Crowley explained that in Gladden's opening statement he more or less conceded guilt and appeared determined to concentrate on the second stage of the proceedings – the case for Degarmo receiving a life sentence rather than the death penalty.

'At that stage,' Crowley said, 'they told the jury that Roger had had a head injury in the past, and there would be evidence of childhood abuse and trauma, and evidence of new scientific techniques that would show that he had brain damage....'

Gladden's aim was to produce pictures for the jury that would be so easy to look at, so simple to comprehend, that no specialized knowledge would be necessary in order to determine there was something wrong with Degarmo's brain.

'My associate likes to use the term "a janitor picture",' Gladden confided. 'What he means by that is that at the end of the day, when the department's closed and there's a study up on the computer monitor, and the janitor comes in and he's mopping the floor, then he sees the picture on the screen and he goes "Wow! That looks terrible!"'

Sid Crowley admitted that at the time of the trial he did not know what a PET scan was. His department set one of their investigators the task of finding out something about this new technology, and he came up with an editorial by Dr Helen Mayberg entitled 'An Argument for Caution in Criminal Courts', which was about the difficulties of forming solid opinions based on PET scans without a sound understanding of their implications.

To illustrate what she had said in the editorial, Dr Mayberg explained just one of numerous difficulties which arise when, as she puts it, 'one tries to move into these more ill-defined behavioural arenas.'

She displayed a series of brain-scan pictures.

'The first scan is of a normal healthy subject. The scan is fairly symmetric and the activity is fairly uniform throughout the entire cortex of the brain. The second scan is really different.'

The brain image appeared irregular and seemed to have large holes in it, whereas the normal scan had been regular and relatively unblemished.

'One whole side of the brain looks wiped out. This is the consequence of a stroke. This patient can't move the right side, can't speak, has had a tremendous clinical problem – but look at picture number three. This also is a stroke patient, the scan looks very abnormal, just like the previous one. You might expect that this person has problems with moving the right side of the body, problems with language and speech – but in fact this patient's clinical problems are completely resolved, they're totally gone and the patient looks great. The question and the problem we have is, how can you use a PET scan to infer what a patient's going to be like, when you can see that a very similar scan pattern can give you wildly different clinical presentations?'

After reading Dr Mayberg's editorial, Sid Crowley contacted her and asked if she would agree to serve as an expert witness for the state.

She agreed, and Crowley took the pictures of Degarmo's brain to San Antonio for her to examine. Her first reaction, she said later, was that the scans had not been carried out as well as they could have been.

'They were technically acceptable, but the subject was actually put into the scanner in a slightly tilted manner.'

When PET scans are being made, a great deal of care is taken to make sure the patient's head is placed exactly straight in the scanner. If the head is tilted, the resulting picture will be asymmetrical, and the image could be construed either as an indication of brain abnormality in a normal case, or that no abnormality exists where in fact there has been damage.

'Fortunately, in such a case, what I can do is use the other views which are made on the computer,' Dr Mayberg explained, *'to allow me to look at that same area of the brain from another orientation, whether it be front-on – re-slicing the brain from front to back – or side-on, as though I'm looking at the brain from the position of the ear. Now, when I look at these images...,'* she indicated Degarmo's brain scans, *'I can't find the one small area of abnormality that I can see on the original slices. I can't find it on either the side view or the front-on view. So my conclusion was that the scan was tilted, that there was this very subtle abnormality in one view in the right frontal lobe, but since it could not be confirmed from other orientations, my conclusion was that the scan was normal.'*

Dr Hickey argued that although there was a slight tilt in Degarmo's position at the time the scan was made, the computer was capable of re-orienting the brain in its own interpretive space, so that the brain appeared perfectly straight.

Not so, said Dr Mayberg.

'I guess what Dr Hickey doesn't understand is that a PET scan is acquired in a single orientation, the horizontal orientation. If that original scan is tilted, the subsequent scans, the other

orientations, all are dependent on that original data set. If the
original is tilted, the subsequent scans will be tilted.'

Sid Crowley mentioned another area of conflicting testimony. Dr
Hickey, he said, testified that the radiologist at the hospital where
the scans were made had agreed with Hickey's reading that the
scans showed brain abnormality. But when Crowley's staff went to
the hospital to obtain a copy of the radiologist's record, they found
it said just the opposite: the radiologist had found no evidence that
Degarmo suffered any degree of abnormal brain activity.

Confronted with this discrepancy today, Dr Hickey chooses to
see it as a matter of interpretation rather than evidence that he
misled the court. Besides, he doesn't think the court is an
appropriate arena for raising such matters.

'The courtroom is no place to have a discussion of the merits of,
you know, anything to do with medicine. It just isn't. It's a
theatrical setting.'

The colour pictures of Roger Degarmo's brain were by no
means the only theatrical feature of his defence. Greg Gladden had
mustered a number of dramatic devices, including the loud,
resonant noise made by the wheel rim that had hit his client in the
face all those years ago. He tapped it a couple of times on a
concrete floor to demonstrate.

'It makes an enormous ruckus,' he said. 'The drama of having
some heavy piece of metal like this up against someone's face at
high velocity – it reduced the prosecution's little bitty unloaded
gun, clicking it in their final argument, to child's play. It
demonstrated there are more victims to this case than just
Kimberley. Roger had been a victim and has probably suffered a
lot more than Kimberley did.'

To do his job Gladden needed to make the jury feel as much
sympathy for his client as he could. In his closing argument, he
talked about his own niece, who suffered brain damage in a car

accident; overcome with emotion, he had to leave his co-counsel to finish. It was a moment Kimberley's mother will never forget.

'Gladden was crying so bad he went and sat down,' she recalled. 'The co-counsel came out with two roses and a picture of Kim. He laid the picture of Kim on the witness stand, and he laid one rose on top of the picture, and he said "This is sad what happened to her...".'

Mrs Strickler was appalled to see him take the other rose between his hands and start picking it apart, a petal at a time, letting the petals drop slowly to the floor.

'This case,' he said, 'just like this rose, is falling all apart, a petal at a time.'

In this emotionally charged atmosphere, Gladden's coup in creating the belief that Roger Degarmo had brain damage left the jury wide open to further suggestion.

'Even though he certainly did kill Kim,' said Mrs Strickler, 'and though he certainly is a continuing threat to society, the defence said that because of mitigating circumstances and because he had a sad childhood, because he had brain damage too, they should give him life. And that's what the jury did.'

Sid Crowley said his department did all they could to get the death penalty for Degarmo. 'We went the extra mile, and when you do that, when you put up a case like we did, when you find a superb expert witness like Dr Mayberg, and still in the end it isn't good enough...' He shrugged. 'You just try to accept it, remind yourself you do your best and that's all you can do.'

The most unfortunate feature of the case, in Dr Mayberg's view, was that the jury was presented with two sides. One said the scan was abnormal, the other said no, the scan was not abnormal. In spite of the probability that the jury would find one witness more credible than the other, the upshot was nevertheless a conflict.

'And that, by definition, raised the issue of reasonable doubt,' Mayberg said. *'Even by having the discussion, no matter what the truth really was, the jury was obligated to have concern and to err on the side of caution.'*

Greg Gladden defends any theatricality on his part by pointing out that there is so much at stake in a murder trial, especially one where the defendant may lose his life, that extreme measures are often necessary if a defence counsel is to do the best he can for his client.

'With all respect to Dr Mayberg,' he said, *'it was just really hard to overcome those big pictures with asymmetrical images that were supposed to be symmetrical.'*

Dr Mayberg says she finds it disgusting that science, instead of being used as a means to bring truth into court, or to interpret for the jury, or to simplify overly technical information – 'is so often used to create bedlam, and to establish goals for subversive and non-scientific reasons'.

Professor Walker has his own views on the presentation of complex testimony to a jury made up of ordinary citizens.

'It's very difficult for a jury of lay people to deal with either an insanity defence, or a defence of diminished responsibility. Technical terms are used by psychiatrists and however good they are at explaining to a jury what they mean, I can't help feeling that it would be better if they had to explain themselves to the judge and, say, a couple of assessors, who would be psychiatrists or psychologists unconnected with the case.'

This arrangement, Walker feels, would avoid the disagreements over technical terms that arise in criminal cases, so very often, because complex matters have to be reduced to simplified language in order to put points across to juries.

'They would be talking to people who had dealt with such cases and such defences before,' he said, *'and the issues would be*

clear to all concerned. I don't think it would be such a revolutionary step to take defence cases of this kind away from juries and give them to a judge with qualified professional assessors.'

The moral of this chapter is that in the legal debates and discussions of sanity and insanity, of guilt and innocence, it is lawyers and not scientists who call the tune. Since insanity is essentially a legal concept it has become the established province of lawyers to decide how and by whom psychiatric evidence will be presented. They can even decide what will be said and what will be left out.

Science is held in high esteem by the public, for it seems to be unique in its lack of bias, and in the objective way it gets at the truth. The trouble is, when scientists go into the courtroom, a lot of what makes science desirable is left outside: the objectivity, the sharing of information, the building of a consensus, the slow accumulation of evidence. So what the juries see is really the popular image of science – the charts, the diagrams, the jargon – and not the substance, not the objectivity, not the things that make science reliable.

There is always a danger that courts will put too much trust in scientific evidence which isn't quite as reliable as they are conditioned to believe it is. That observation does not only apply to forensic psychiatry, it goes for all forensic science. We need to bear in mind that what we see in the courtroom is controlled by a lawyer, and lawyers are paid to take sides.

buried
witne

North of Honduras and El Salvador and south of Mexico lies the Republic of Guatemala, Central America's third largest country and one of its most visually impressive. Two thirds of the land area is made up of mountains, many of them volcanic, and vast stretches of the country are covered by a tropical forest called the Petén. There are countless oak and pine forests, a shore-to-shore abundance of flowering plants and a huge population of exotic, colourful birds – the national symbol is the gaudy quetzal parrot. There are people too, 9.7 million of them, the majority of whom are Mayan Indians, who live in towns and villages in the highland region dominating the southern half of the country.

Paradoxically in a society that is mainly agricultural, and where fertile soil is an abundant resource, large numbers of Guatemala's people are seriously undernourished. Diseases of deprivation thrive there; malnutrition accounts for more than half the annual deaths. Life expectancy, at birth, is 61 years for a boy, 66 for a girl. Programmes of social welfare are badly organized, poorly implemented and pathetically out of date. Health care in the communities outside the capital city is either inadequate or non-existent.

sses

The Mayans have come down in the world. Long before the Spanish conquered Mexico and Central America, the ancient Mayan Indians had one of the greatest civilizations ever to flourish in the western hemisphere. Many of its impressive remains lie within the borders of Guatemala, where the ruins of towns, temple pyramids and spectacular plazas can be seen throughout the country, even in the remotest areas. For many years archaeologists and historians have gone to Guatemala to study the Mayan culture, their religion and their architecture. Some of the older traditions survive among today's hill people, but internal wars, natural catastrophes and too many years of bad administration have diminished the Mayan character.

In June, 1994, a team of specialists came to the village of Plan de Sanchez in the lower mountains of Central Guatemala. They were Stefan Schmitt, Andy Kaufman, Federico Reyes Lopez, Fernando Moscoso and Mariana Valdizón, a new breed of investigative scientists, young and appropriately skilled for the job they had been invited to tackle. Unlike other visiting scientists, they had not arrived at Plan de Sanchez to study the remains of an ancient civilization: they had come to investigate a modern-day atrocity.

Originally trained as archaeologists, the team was working on the Mayan ruins when one of them saw an advertisement in a national newspaper, inviting archaeologists to add anthropology to their qualifications and help create a Guatemalan forensic team. 'The idea,' said Andy Kaufman, 'was that it would be an institution in which everyone of us would be replaceable. But each of us have our strong points, but we like to feel that each team member can do the jobs of the others. For example, Fernando is a wonderful archaeologist, but he also knows how to analyse bones. Stefan is a bone expert bu the also knows about archaeology. I know how to analyse bones but my strong point might be more like placing our work in a context of human rights documentation – I like to meet with the family members and explain the process to them.'

The group was trained by Dr Clyde Snow, an American pioneer

in the field of forensic anthropology who, since the late 1960s, has specialized in investigations of human rights violations.

The Guatemala forensic team went to Plan de Sanchez at the invitation of the government. They would work under the direct supervision of Clyde Snow, and they would employ a range of skills in an effort to make accurate interpretations of past events. They were taking on dangerous work, because a number of quite ruthless people, some of them powerful political and military figures, would be upset by the planned operation. 'We're risking our lives,' said Andy, 'because the civil patrols have guns, and they are the authority in the countryside.'

Nevertheless the team remained objective and determined, as scientists must. Their task was to discover what really happened in Plan de Sanchez 12 years before, when more than a hundred villagers were allegedly massacred by soldiers of their own government.

The 18th of July 1982 was a Sunday, and like every Sunday in the region it was market day. Many of the villagers of Plan de Sanchez made their weekly two-hour journey down the mountain to the town of Rabinal to sell their wares.

Around midday, after a morning's trading, people began returning to their villages. Domingo, an eyewitness, was one of those making his way back to Plan de Sanchez with his family.

'On our way to the village we saw the soldiers,' he said. *'They were climbing up behind us. There were about 60 of them.'*

At that time Guatemala was in the grip of severe political upheaval. In March, two weeks after the election of a new president, a military coup had installed a three-man junta headed by General Efraín Ríos Montt. In June, Montt dissolved the junta and assumed the presidency, ruling as a dictator. When the left-wing guerrillas spurned his offer of an amnesty and swore to continue opposing him, Montt organized ferocious anti-guerrilla actions by his soldiers in the countryside.

'That afternoon, that Sunday,' said another witness, Juan Manuel, 'I left my family here....' He pointed to an area at the north of the village. 'I went back to our house lower down the hill. When I got there, the soldiers were collecting everybody from their homes. I tried to get back to my family, I tried to see them, but the soldiers were there, they had rounded them all into my sister's house.'

Juan Manuel's brother, Salvador, was 12 at the time. 'I saw them,' he said. 'They brought all my family, and the family of my grandmother and my aunt... I didn't want to get closer because I would have been caught, so I climbed that hill there and I hid behind a tree.'

From his hiding place Salvador heard the first burst of gunfire, then another. By that time, Domingo had reached the edge of the village. He heard the guns too, then one of the soldiers shouting 'You little shits!' Immediately there was more firing.

'After the shooting I saw them separating a group of young women from the others,' Salvador said. 'They marched them down the hill and into one of the houses there.'

Recalling how he felt in the immediate aftermath, Juan Manuel said, 'We felt totally destroyed, both mentally and physically. The only consolation that we had was that I knew a few of God's words. That is what I reflected upon the day after the massacre. We could no longer live or work or think. What could we do with our lives? After that, many times, we started to drink, because really, if I didn't drink, the pain would not go away. We drank because of the pain and the feelings we had for our families.'

Hidden behind a tree, the young boy witnessed the girls being sexually violated, tortured, then shot.

'My nieces were raped. I heard them, I saw it, and all the time they were being raped I could hear those girls screaming....'

The survivors alleged that the soldiers were accompanied by three civilians whom they recognized as neighbours, the sons of a local landowner called Francisco Orego. According to the survivors, the three brothers picked out those who were killed; the villagers believed it was the father of these three men who persuaded the army that Plan de Sanchez was a guerrilla base.

'What they want is to put the blame on me,' Francisco Orego complained. 'How could I know what was happening over there when I live here? Neither I nor my sons live over there – we have land there, and we plant crops, but we do not live there.'

Señor Orego's feeble defence continued with the allegation that the villagers themselves were less innocent than the survivors claimed, and that they were killed in a battle between the guerrillas and the army.

'At that time the guerrillas were over here, over there, they were everywhere,' Orego said, 'and those people – I don't know if it is because they are ignorant, or why they did it – were feeding the guerrillas and supporting them.'

On the day in question Orego alleged the army were told that guerrillas were in Plan de Sanchez. When the soldiers arrived they crept up and surrounded the village in an attempt to capture the guerrillas.

'That's when the soldiers say that the guerrillas started firing at them,' Orego said. 'And that's how it all happened.'

This kind of claim and counter-claim, says Clyde Snow, with civilian witnesses on the one hand saying their people were victims of an unprovoked massacre, and the army on the other side saying the people were either killed in crossfire or because they were fighting the army, is very common.

'And of course, both sides have a vested interest in maintaining their story,' said Snow. 'Under these circumstances there's only one way to find the truth, and that's to examine the physical

evidence – open up the graves and take a look at the bones and the bullets and see what they tell us. That's the only way I know to get at the truth of these very important and terrible events.'

The day after the killings the villagers were apparently given only a few hours to bury their dead. The first step in the investigation was to find out what the survivors remembered about the bodies they buried. This was a vital part of making a case, since the more details the exhumations confirmed, the more likely it would be that the villagers were telling the truth.

Statements were taken before the team opened grave number nine, one of 24 they had identified. This grave would be a vital test case, a sample to check whether the truth could be uncovered in this way, and if so, whose story could be verified.

Domingo and Juan Manuel remembered burying four of the raped women and a young boy in grave number nine.

'I found my sister-in-law, Maria Dolores, all complete, not burned, but raped and tortured,' Juan Manuel said. 'Her arms were tied behind her back.' He also remembered that when he buried her she was wearing the necklace he had given her for her wedding. It was a detail which could be crucial in identifying her remains.

Meanwhile, Domingo remembered seeing that one of the victims, his niece Ismelda, had had her right arm cut off by a machete. As this and other details were recalled they were diligently written down.

The opening of the grave was begun. In nearly every respect it was conducted like an archaeological dig. Soil was removed methodically and to a regular pattern, so that the earth level dropped evenly across the length and breadth of the site. As the soil and clay were removed they were carefully examined for artefacts. Photographs were taken at each of the phases of the dig and soil was retained at various levels for analysis. Notes and drawings were made, so that the continuity of the exhumation was recorded in detail, care being taken to avoid gaps in the record.

Human remains gradually became visible. As is customary in an archaeological dig, the bodies were not lifted out of the ground: instead, a folded blanket covering them was first moved aside, then the earth was taken away from around the bodies a little at a time, so that no part of the bodies was lost or unduly disturbed. By meticulous stages the remains were isolated from their surroundings. After three days of progressively cautious digging, four skeletons were now detectable to the trained eye. A little later, signs of a fifth and much smaller skeleton became visible.

'It's important to recover every bone, every tooth and every bullet,' Snow said, 'because each of these objects tells you something about that individual. The human skeleton consists of around 200 bones and 32 teeth, and even the tiniest one of those, sometimes, can tell you about that person's age, sex, race or old injuries.'

Nothing was allowed to escape attention, and quite apart from the fragments of evidence, the open grave itself had a distinct value in the investigation: because it was the context of the burial, it was a valuable aid towards reconstructing the event.

'In a kind of an elementary way,' Snow explained, 'space translates into time. Something as simple as, for instance, this body being on top of another body, means that the topmost body went into the grave last.' Old circumstances emerged from the tableau which was so painstakingly released from the earth.

'This is what we're trying to bring into the courtroom – the story, not just a collection of plastic bags with bullets or bones in them.'

After four days of excavation work, the bodies were almost ready to be taken away from the grave where they had lain for 12 years. To the Mayans this was an occasion for religious ceremony. They believe that buried bodies cannot be exhumed without their spirits growing angry, therefore God has to be warned, so that he can grant his approval and thereby placate the troubled dead.

'The same grief came back that we had on the day they suffered so, the day of the massacre,' said Juan Manuel. 'We remembered great pain and many thoughts came back.'

So far, as they had been uncovering the bodies, the scientists worked with the assumption that there were five people in the grave, four of them women, the other a child of about ten. Up to that point, the remains tallied with the villagers' statements.

'If we find the skeletons have the characteristics we have been told about,' one of the team said, 'we can show that the testimonies are compatible with reality. This could help a lot towards positive identification of the remains.'

Clyde Snow examined the topmost skeleton prior to its removal, handling the bones carefully to avoid disturbing their relative positions. Each time he confronts a new exhumation, a forensic anthropologist must try to answer eight fundamental questions, or as many of them as he can: 1: Are the bones real? 2: Are they human remains? 3: What is their sex? 4: What was the height and general build of the deceased? 5: Are there clear indications of race? 6: What was the approximate age of the individual at the time of death? 7: How long has the body been buried? 8: Cause of death?

'One of the victims, we were told, had had her arm removed with a machete. We don't know if it was at the time of death or after death, but, indeed...' Snow felt carefully among the bones; 'here is a roughly mid-teen female, and here's the left arm, it was thrown over her lower face – but the right arm bones are missing. Now under this fabric here I can feel the humerus and it has a smooth cut mark, so this is the girl who had her arm amputated.'

The second skeleton to be removed had a necklace halfway inside the mouth. There was also a circle of tightly-braided hair still attached to the top of the skull.

As the team took away the remains, every bone, bullet and scrap of clothing was examined and a record made of its position relative to the other fragments, so that individual skeletons could be fully reassembled in the laboratory together with their surrounding material. As the exhumation progressed to its final stages, the skeleton at the bottom of the grave was found to have a shattered skull.

Finally the grave was empty; the team had uncovered four women's skeletons and that of a half-burned child. But just as they were ready to leave, they made an unexpected discovery.

'We found another skeleton,' a team member said. 'Apparently there were two children in this grave. We took the blanket that we pulled off at the beginning, which had been doubled over, and when we opened it to see if there were bullet fragments or anything like that in it, we found a child's skeleton inside. With it being such a small skeleton it was very light and easy to miss. So we've found a sixth skeleton we didn't know about. We were told there were five.'

As the team prepared to take the skeletons to the laboratory for intensive study, history was in the making in Guatemala. In only the second democratic election in 50 years, the people were voting for 80 new Congress members. One of the hot favourites for high office was the former dictator, General Efraín Ríos Montt, whose soldiers were believed to have played a key part in the events at Plan de Sanchez on Sunday, 18 July 1982.

Although anthropology is literally 'the science of man', in practical terms it can be any combination of several disciplines concerned with human beings. The anthropologists' approach differs from that of physiologists and psychologists by concentrating on group variations in human physique and mentality. A further distinction is that anthropologists interpret the special characteristics of a group of people, or group activity, in terms of its time and place in human history.

The techniques of present-day anthropology take in a range of specialities from the physical, biological, behavioural and social sciences. For example, atomic physics has contributed radiocarbon dating for estimating the relative ages of archaeological finds; haematological procedures developed for examining the inheritance of blood types have made it possible for anthropologists to determine, among many other things, that European gypsies originally came from India; psychological principles have been used by anthropologists to clarify family relationships, explain the growth of rituals and taboos, and tabulate the development of religious traditions among different peoples.

Forensic anthropology, Clyde Snow's speciality, applies the art and multi-faceted science of anthropology to the purposes of law.

Speaking of the investigation at Plan de Sanchez, Snow said, 'We have the responsibility to bring this evidence to light – even though it is not used in courts to put the bad guys in jail – simply to put it on the historical record, to document it. Our science, in particular, is hard to argue with. It's hard to argue with a skull with a bullet in it, so this keeps the revisionists from coming along 20 or 30 or 50 years later and saying, "These things didn't happen," like we're seeing now, where people are maintaining the Holocaust never, never happened.'

To find answers required by the law the forensic scientist must try to re-create the past from the evidence on hand, and he must do it in terms that can be proved. To any scientist investigating possible murder, dead bodies are the most important resource, but dead bodies decay quickly, and the more tissue is decomposed, the less useful it is to the scientist. Bones, on the other hand, can last for decades and even centuries, and so they provide a rich source of study for the forensic scientist who must unravel and reconstruct old crimes.

The classification of skeletons calls for patient study, since there are huge variations between sexual and racial types, as well as between individuals within each of the groups. In general, the sex, race, height and age of remains can be established in stages, as follows:

- *the sex of a skeleton will be determined principally from the skull and pelvis*
- *indications of race are found most frequently in the skull and teeth*
- *height is gauged by direct measurement of long bones*
- *estimations of age are made from examination of the centres of ossification (i.e. areas where growing cartilage has been replaced to a lesser or greater extent with bone), and the areas where maturity can be measured by the fusion of bones.*

Only those who have worked in the field for a long time will know they are handling something that deviates from normal to such a degree that it can be called unique – so eminently unique, sometimes, that it will make nonsense of the hard rules slavishly followed by less experienced scientists.

At 8.00 a.m. on the day following the removal of the skeletons from grave nine, Snow and his colleagues began work in the laboratory. The bones of the six skeletons were laid out as nearly as possible in the correct anatomical positions. This would provide some direct indication of stature; it would also help in assessing the presence and extent of wounds and other damage. The first big step in such an investigation, however, is to sex each skeleton.

The most valuable – and least difficult – part of the skeleton to use for sexing human remains is the pelvis. Since the female pelvis is capable of supporting pregnancy it has enough points of difference, usually, to make it easy to identify. There are still occasions, however, where a pelvis will show mixed male and female characteristics, and in such cases an opinion about the sex has to be limited to one of greater or lesser probability.

Favoured techniques for interpreting signs from the pelvis vary widely from one practitioner to another. This table of comparative features shows areas of broad agreement among authorities.

MALE	FEMALE
Framework massive.	*Much less bulky.*
Deep, more 'upright'.	*Shallow, capacious.*
Walls not splayed.	*Walls splayed.*
Thigh sockets large, average 52 mm diameter, and they face sideways.	*Thigh sockets 46 mm average diameter, facing part front, part sideways.*
Sacrum relatively narrow and long, its curve being equal over its whole length.	*Sacrum wide and short, curve confined to a point starting below centre of the third vertebra.*
————	*The various diameters (side-to-side, oblique, front-to-back) are greater than in the male.*
————	*The pelvic outlet has been described as 'roomy', and admits the passage of a clenched fist.*

The inominate bone (consisting of the hip bone, the ilium, the ischium and the pubis) is often the only major fragment found at burial sites. Even though it forms just a part of the pelvis, the inominate can, on its own, be a trustworthy guide to the sex of its former owner. Several specialists have claimed better than 75 per cent success in estimating sex from the angle formed by the sides of the greater sciatic notch, which is situated behind the inominate bone. The notch is much wider in women (nearer to a right angle) than it is in men.

'When we articulate the three bones that make up the pelvis,' Snow said, 'the two hip bones, right and left, and the sacrum which is the base of the spine, we can look at this angle here....' He pointed to an inverted V shape at the front of the pelvis, with its apex under the pubic bone: 'We call it the sub-pubic angle, and that is much broader in females than it is in males.'

He then demonstrated a handy rule for determining sex from the sub-pubic angle.

'In males it's about as wide as the angle you can make between your middle and index fingers; in females it's about as wide as the angle you can make between your forefinger and your thumb.'

There are a lot of guidelines for determining sex from evidence detectable on a skull, but many of them are contradictory. The following is an abbreviated list used by pathologists and anthropologists as a guide in determining the sex of adult skeletons. Skulls of younger people are evaluated using variations on these and other criteria.

A: In general appearance the female skull is smoother and much more rounded than the male.

B: The female skull is smaller; the internal capacity is about 6.5 fluid ounces (200 ml) less than the male.

C: The supra-orbital ridges – bony 'eyebrow' lines – are more prominent in men and may be completely absent in women.

D: The mastoid process, which is the bump immediately behind the ear, is much larger in males than in females.

E: A woman's temporal and parietal regions (temples and central upper parts of the skull) remain much closer to the prominent childhood formation than they do in men.

F: The male palate tends to be of a regular U shape, whereas in women it is smaller and has been described as parabolic.

G: The eye sockets are set lower on the face of the male skull; they are more nearly rectangular than in the female and the edges are less sharply defined, especially along the upper margin.

H: The male's nasal aperture is higher and narrower then the female's. Male nasal bones are larger; they protrude more and meet at a sharper angle than in the female.

I: In the female skull the forehead is high and far more rounded than in the male.

J: Female teeth are smaller, the molars usually having four cusps. The lower first molars in the male commonly have five cusps.

K: The male has a larger jaw, and it is squarer at the front where the two jaw bones unite; at this point, too, the male jaw is longer vertically than the female. The angle where the jawbone turns upward at the sides is more upright in the male, usually less than 125 degrees.

When no skull or pelvis is available, the investigator often determines the sex of remains by relying on calculations based on long-bone characteristics and measurements. The femur is favourite for this work – even allowing for the inevitable overlap of long-bone sexual characteristics, most anthropologists and pathologists defend the femur's reliability as an indicator. It has been shown that the maximum length for a male femur is 459 mm, while the female maximum is 426. A commonly used working range is 390 – 407 mm for women and 430 – 450 for men, with an overlap in the mid-range.

The size of the head of the femur is reckoned by some people to be a more reliable guide, the vertical diameter being on average greater than 45 mm in the male and less than 41 mm in the female. Then again, a few investigators place importance on the sternum (breastbone) as an indicator of sex. As with other narrow bones, differences of length and proportion between the sexes are the basis for a complex series of tabular calculations.

Estimating a person's age from the skeleton is a more difficult job. While measurements of bone length are an obvious approach in assessing the age of someone who died in childhood, a way to pinpoint the age more accurately is to examine the bone formation at certain areas – called ossification centres – where cartilage gives way to bone as the person gets older. The closure of the bones in the skull is another indication of age in younger people (old people, too), and so is the development of the teeth.

Estimating the age of someone in the range of child-to-young-adult can sometimes be accurate to within months by careful study of the ossification centres (as above) and the extent of epiphyseal fusion, which is the joining of the end parts of long bones, which in the early stages of life grow separately from the shaft. For example, the head of the femur will be partly fused in a 16-year-old, whereas fusion will be complete by the age of 19; the joining of the collarbone to the top of the breastbone will be partial at 23 years, but not complete until approximately 28 years. In this category teeth are also a useful guide to age.

For estimating the age of older people, the following rules are said to be accurate to within a decade:
- *skull suture fusion (least accurate)*
- *changes in pubic bone pattern*

- **tooth wear**
- **arthritic changes in bones.**

To gauge the height from a complete skeleton, it is fairly easy to reassemble it and measure the length directly, although this will never give an accurate indication of the person's stature when he or she was alive. For one thing, the unknown thickness of scalp and heel tissue has to be added to the total length; then there are the even more uncertain factors of spinal disc thickness and thickness of joint cartilage. All in all, it would be unrealistic to expect an accuracy of less than 4 cm compared to the living height of the subject.

When no complete skeleton is available, calculations of stature have to be made from long bones. Wherever it is possible, all available bones are used and the results are assessed collectively, to give the investigators an optimum estimation of the dead person's height. The level of accuracy varies depending on the bones available, which in descending order of usefulness are the femur, tibia, humerus and radius.

A number of formulas have been published for determining the height of an individual from their bones. Anthropologists have always seen this as an area of research where very important results could be achieved if solid standards were developed and rigorously maintained. As long ago as 1863 a French physician, Luca, came up with these research notes on the relative length of the bones of the human skeleton.

- **The length of the head equals one eighth of the total body height.**
- **The head is divided into two equal parts by a line drawn just under the eyes; each of these parts equals one 16th the total body height.**
- **The nostrils subdivide the lower half of the face equally; each of the resulting parts is equal to one 32nd of the total body height.**

- *The pubis is a central point between the two extremes of the body, so head to pubis, or pubis to the soles of the feet, equals one half of the total body height.*
- *The height of a man equals the distance which separates the extremities of the hands when the arms are extended in a horizontal line from the body.*
- *The upper extremities can be divided into five parts: the hand represents one part, the forearm two parts, and the upper arm two parts. The elbow is the boundary between the lower and upper arm.*
- *Regardless of the length of the hand, five times its length equals the whole of the length of the whole upper extremity.*
- *Half the length of the hand equals the length of the area occupied by the carpal and metacarpal bones.*

Although that list has some value, the tables most commonly used, because they are comprehensive and relatively accurate, are those by Karl Pearson, first published in 1899. Tables published by Dupertuis and Hadden in 1951 are also in common use among anthropologists, archaeologists and pathologists.

The tables and their formulas have to be used with caution, even by the most experienced investigators. They were constructed from data taken from both black and white racial groups at widely different times, therefore ethnic and nutritional variations occur and are bound to distort the results. Matters get complicated further in cases where the race of the dead person can't be determined beforehand.

Another factor likely to cloud the results is the difference in average height between the sexes; the process of ageing also makes a person shorter. Two leading researchers in the field of estimating stature, the Americans Trotter and Gleser, noted in an examination of nearly 900 bodies that there was a 1.2 cm loss of height for each 20-year period after the age of 30, which is consistent with a height loss of about 0.6 mm per year after the age of 40. During the same investigation Trotter and Gleser found that dead bodies were about 2.5 cm longer than their known height in life. Maximum stature in American men was found to be reached at about the age of 23. This contradicts other authorities who claim the peak is reached between 18 and 21.

In spite of all the uncertainties in the available methods, good and valuable estimates of human height are regularly made from the evidence of bones.

By examining pelvic bones from grave nine, and the points of incomplete fusion on some of the long bones, the Guatemala team determined they had found the skeletons of young women in the mid-to-late-teen range. They also discovered that the skeleton with the missing arm and the one with the shattered skull were the remains of teenage girls of approximately the same height and age. This clinched the testimony of Domingo and Juan Manuel, who said they buried two 17-year-olds in that grave – Ismelda Cajbon Grave and Dominga Corazón Geronimo.

In summing up his team's findings, Clyde Snow spoke with the experience and insight of a man who has supervised hundreds of similar investigations in locations all over the world. His justification for ascribing identities to the two skeletons highlighted the terrible violence suffered by both girls.

'This particular skeleton is a mid-teenage female,' he said, pointing to the skeleton with the severed arm. 'She is the age of Ismelda, and she indeed has a complete diagonal cut mark across the bone of her upper right arm.

'The other skeleton within this age range doesn't have this injury. Witnesses mentioned a lot of blood on the chest of the second teenage girl, Dominga, and I think we can see where that came from. Over here...', he pointed to a greenish metal shard lodged in the fragile bone. '...In the fifth chest vertebra, there is a fragment from the metal jacket of a bullet. Apparently a bullet entered more or less from her right side towards the back,

*travelled transversely and part of it lodged in the vertebra after it
had broken a couple of ribs.'*

There were further ribcage injuries caused by another bullet;
the accumulated damage to the girl's chest would certainly have
been enough to cause death. However, when Dominga's skull had
been reassembled and the broken bones glued together, further
terrible injury came to light.

*'Unlike what we see in many other countries, where we find a
single gunshot wound in the back of the head – it's the
trademark of the executioner throughout the world – here we
have a gunshot wound low at the back of the skull, elongated
like a keyhole, hence they're called keyhole entry wounds. It tells
us the bullet was travelling from the left to the right at a rather
shallow angle. Now, I suspect that the bullet began to break up,
and a number of the fragments passed downward, causing
some of the damage we see to the base of the skull. Some
perhaps even went down into the lower jaw, and still other
fragments could have come off those and travelled into the
neck, causing the fractures we found in the upper neck
vertebrae known as the atlas and the axis.*

'Now in addition to the gunshot wound, over on this side...,'
Snow pointed to a long slash in the bone of the forehead,
diagonally over the left eye socket. *'This is a very even cut mark,
which is characteristic of the machetes which are used down
here very frequently, either in killing people or to make post-
mortem mutilations. At some point or another, someone
whacked her across the forehead with a machete, causing this
cut.'*

There were other smaller machete marks on the skull, and
overall, Dominga had suffered so many serious injuries that it would
have been very difficult to pinpoint a single cause of death.

At Plan de Sanchez, Snow decided, there was abundant
evidence of homicide. Dominga alone, with her shattered skull and

bullet-riddled body, was clearly a victim of unlawful killing.

'This was a terrible way to die,' Snow said. 'Sometimes I think being dead is no problem, it's getting there that's tough. Dominga had a tough time getting there. And we multiply her case many times, because we know that at least 110 people, men women and children, died up there in Plan de Sanchez on that July afternoon.'

The skeleton with the necklace in its mouth and the ring of braided hair on the skull was identified as Juan Manuel's sister-in-law. The first child to be found had a shattered lower leg. The only child of ten who was reportedly buried in grave nine had lost his left leg; his name was Rodrigo Cajbon Grave. Metal fragments found nearby and imbedded in the bones of his right leg were identified as pieces of bullets, indicating that he was shot and may well have bled to death.

The mysterious sixth body was identified as a seven-year-old girl, Juana Cajbon Grave, Rodrigo's younger sister. His older sister was Ismelda, the girl whose arm was cut off. All the children of the Cajbon Grave family had been killed.

In all, the remains of 40 children would be found at Plan de Sanchez, 19 of them under 10 years old. Several had gunshot wounds, others were too badly burned to be identified.

At approximately the time more graves were being opened at Plan de Sanchez, the Guatemalan Congress was about to swear in its new members. As expected, General Ríos Montt was one of them. The group he led was now the biggest in Congress. The theme of his campaign was that there could be no peace in Guatemala without justice.

'I have been touring the country,' he told a representative of the investigative team, 'and lately, with the discovery of the clandestine graves at Plan de Sanchez, I was very shocked and I went to see what had happened.' He claimed that his

predecessors in power had ordered such killings across the country, and he was keen that justice should be done. 'This is something I would very much like you to investigate, because this is something to which I must have an answer.'

The villagers of Plan de Sanchez remained adamant that the army carried out the massacre. The only direct evidence of the source of the killings were bullets found in the ground with the skeletons.

Bullets and spent cartridge cases can tell an investigator a great deal. Gun design also has a lot to do with the outcome of the investigative process. In the revolver, the self-loading pistol and the rifle, all of them single-shot-firing weapons, it is possible to stabilize the bullet. This process begins during its travel along the barrel, where the manufacturer puts so-called 'rifling' into the gun.

Rifling is a series of grooves cut longitudinally into the barrel's inner surface; the grooves are parallel and they run in a spiral formation from breech to muzzle. This makes the bullet spin on its axis as it is fired. The raised spaces between the grooves are called lands. As the bullet travels at high velocity along the barrel its surface is in close contact with these lands, which force it into a spin. When the bullet leaves the barrel the spin exerts a gyroscopic, stabilizing action, which enhances accuracy and impact.

A fired bullet, therefore, shows indentations of a parallel series of slanting grooves, usually between four and seven in number, made by the lands inside the gun barrel. The pattern of the rifling in guns of different makes will vary in the number of grooves and the direction of the rifling, so the markings on a fired bullet virtually carry the signature of the gun's manufacturer.

Cartridge cases can also be used to identify the type of weapon, or the actual gun they were fired from. Ammunition carries precise serial numbers, and the gun itself imparts distinctive markings to the case from its breech-face and striker. In self-loading and automatic weapons, the ejector mark on the fired cartridge can be compared with the markings on the metal block which ejects the spent case.

At the time of the killings at Plan de Sanchez, the government soldiers were armed with American M1 and M16 weapons, and Israeli Galils. The guerrillas, on the other hand, used Kalashnikovs. So a battle between army and guerrillas would have left behind very clear evidence about who did the shooting, and where.

Over 50 spent cartridge cases were recovered from the exhumation, together with dozens of bullet fragments. They were all the same calibre – 5.56mm. Every cartridge case is stamped with marks indicating the date of manufacture: in this instance they were made in 1982, the year of the massacre. Other marks showed that the cases found in the clandestine grave were manufactured in Israel and were, in fact, ammunition for the army's Galil and M16 weapons. The markings of the bullets confirmed that they all came from the same group of weapons.

Painstaking and exhaustive investigation at the burial site revealed no evidence of a battle between the guerrillas and the army.

'We've got good, solid, forensic evidence that these people were victims of a massacre, committed by forces of their own government,' said Clyde Snow. Whether or not justice would ever be served, he added, it was still worth the effort to find out precisely how the people died, and to set the record straight.

According to the villagers, the man in charge of the massacre was Lieutenant Roberto Díaz. While the forensic investigation was still underway, Díaz was shot and killed by two men, in front of his wife and children.

It was pointed out to Ríos Montt that the killings at Plan de Sanchez did not happen under his predecessors, as he had claimed, but when he himself was the army commander and so they were committed under the sanction of his presidency.

'That's not true, that's not true,' he replied. 'I have told you my view of what happened. Others may say differently, that's fine. I can take you to those people who were there. You can come with me to Congress. That is all I have to say.'

He refused to answer any more questions. Later, villagers revealed that soldiers had been warning them not to talk to the scientists.

A confidential human rights report, leaked to the producers of the BBC film about the massacre at Plan de Sanchez, reveals that in fact, under Ríos Montt, Plan de Sanchez was only one of seven villages in the area razed to the ground, and this crime was repeated over and over again, across the whole of Guatemala. With the victims and their killers identified, the motive began to emerge. The Guatemalan army was intent on destroying all those who might give support and succour to the guerrillas. So all over Guatemala, they destroyed villages and massacred the inhabitants.

This act of multiple crime against the Mayans was nothing short of genocide.

'The real tragedy of this,' said Clyde Snow, 'is it's not confined to Guatemala. I've seen this sort of thing all over the world. The evidence that science has brought to light in these cases is, in a way, a tool that the advocates involved in the justice process on both sides can use. But like any other tool it can be used correctly, it can be misused, or it can be ignored. Based on the track record that we've seen here in Guatemala over the years, I suspect that it will not be used at all.'

Even so, Clyde Snow and his team are not despondent. They are, after all, pure seekers after truth, no matter where the truth leads them, and no one who is determined to penetrate a social underbrush of lies, deceit and coercion can stay disheartened for long.

'I think there's good evidence that where we can get in and tell the world what happened,' Snow said, 'it actually does act as a deterrent to the killers. Usually it's said that history is written by the winners. But with the help of science, history can be truth.'

white collars, white

coats

Dozens of times a week in America, and with growing frequency in Britain, cellular telephones are being stolen without ever leaving their owners' possession. The crime is committed in seconds, the thief might be only ten metres away, and he leaves no trail worth following. Within minutes the telephone number and other identifying information can be inside another instrument and, every time the bogus phone is used, the call is charged to the original owner.

Cellular bandits operate in the busy commercial districts of major cities where on average they can pick up ten numbers an hour. To obtain the numbers a thief has to do no more than sit with a UHF scanner in a stationary car at the roadside, or stand on an overpass, snatching identities from cellular phones in passing cars.

There have been attempts by manufacturers to build in safeguards, but the biggest obstacle to effective cellular phone security remains the fact that they send their signals through the open air, where invisible plunder has become child's play.

'As soon as the phone is turned on,' a specialist investigator says, 'a lot of information becomes airborne, and because it's in the air it's vulnerable. It can be caught and analysed and duplicated. Fast.'

Security devices introduced by the communications industry during the past couple of years have included screening tones, output-code scramblers and a number of call-delay tactics. All were aimed specifically at curbing the power of the bandits, but they were largely unsuccessful. Most were unwieldy, expensive and only patchily effective. In any case, the bandits eventually have found ways to defeat any security strategies, no matter how ingenious they are.

'On the creative side of this kind of crime, we are dealing with enthusiasts,' the investigator says. 'They're in it for the challenge as well as the money, and a lot of them are undeniably brilliant. They know that if a signal travels through the air, no one can stop it being snatched, and they are just the guys to snatch it – unscramble it, too, if they have to. They've got intuition about the technology and for finding ways around barriers, and a lot of their thinking's way ahead of anything that's working on the side of the angels.'

The information trapped by a scanner can be transferred to other telephone units with the help of a computer and a few simple tools. Cellular telephone theft is in every respect a small-scale, low-profile business that can be operated from the most modest home without drawing attention to itself. But it turns in profits on a scale unimaginable only a few years ago. There are an estimated 25 million cellular telephones in use in the United States, growing at 17 000 a day. Losses to bandits worldwide last year amounted to more than $3 billion.

'Now that the crooks have this electronic theft down to such a smooth operation,' the investigator says, 'the cellular phone has to be one of the most stealable items a person can spend his cash on. And when one gets stolen, the owner's always the last guy to know about it. I mean, these are felons who don't even have to get close, and after the theft, the victim still has the goods right on him.'

The grim truth is that the only way to prevent the identity of a cellular telephone being stolen is to keep it permanently switched off. When the owner makes a call, his instrument sends out four pieces of information: the Electronic Security Number, the Mobile Identification Number, the instrument's Station Class Mark, and the number which is being called. These items are transmitted in a single short burst of data, which is the buzz heard immediately after the caller presses the 'send' button. This buzz contains all that a thief will need to set up a counterfeit telephone which the operating company will believe is the real thing.

Small-time bandits with limited resources have been helped to get started by the fact that American cellular telephone networks occupy frequencies previously assigned to commercial television stations. Two hundred cellular channels will fit into one UHF television channel. So, with simple modification, an old TV set with variable tuning can be made to home-in on all cellular frequencies within a commonly used frequency range.

'A guy can sit up on the roof with one of those hooked up to the power,' the investigator says, 'then he wires the tuner between a 30-to-50-megahertz scanner and a UHF antenna, and he's in business.'

On the other hand, if he has a few hundred dollars to spare, he can buy a highly sensitive portable UHF scanner that fits easily into a pocket. This has the advantage of mobility, which means the operator is harder to pin down, and he can simultaneously widen his choice of units to steal. Even when the telephone company realizes that a particular phone is a fake, their chances of catching the user are slender, since he will know that he has the choice of keeping on the move, or using a different telephone identity every few days.

'The cellular service has the best chance of trapping a bootleg phone user who doesn't move around much,' says the investigator. 'He's usually a wet-eared amateur. He's the kind that develops traceable habits, like calling the same number all

the time from the same place, or doing something really dumb like ordering a pizza.'

Operators at the top end of the cellular-theft scam will re-program the main chip from a stolen or cut-off telephone, giving it an identity that was lifted from the phone of a legitimate user as he drove, say, under a bridge where a bandit stood with his scanner switched on. A laptop computer can be brought to the roadside or on to the bridge where it will transfer the data from the scanner to its own hard disk. The configurations of dozens of telephones can be held simultaneously on the laptop, so the individuals operating the scanners can stay on the job and need never go near the processing end of the operation. From the computer, separate identities can be fed via special software into telephone chips, which are inserted in a programming unit plugged into the back of the computer. The procedure takes only minutes.

The traffic in 'identity-transferred' telephones is only one of many branches of computer crime.

'Almost any area of crime nowadays seems to have a computer or a cellular phone related to it,' says Mark Spooner, a United States Secret Service agent and forensic computer expert, based in Washington DC. 'From drug dealers to counterfeiters to credit card thieves and kidnappers – just about any crime we see now has a connection with either a computer or a cellular phone.'

Spooner explains that, when he is investigating cellular telephone theft, if the only evidence available is a group of telephones, every care is taken to preserve them as they were found. That is to make sure no suspicion of government tampering can be raised by defence counsel when the case goes to court.

'When the evidence comes in, the software is immediately pulled off the chip within the phone, and that chip and that phone are then locked away. We do not work on the physical evidence – it is all paperwork, or copies of software pulled from the original evidence.'

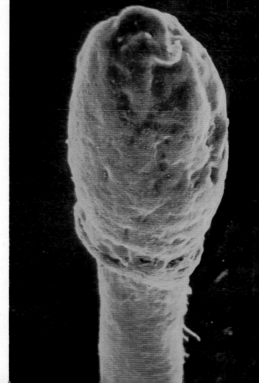

ABOVE AND INSET 'Jailhouse Poet', Jack Unterweger – perhaps the world's first international serial killer. Unterweger achieved celebrity status in his native Austria as a writer while serving a life sentence for murder. He was released from prison early, but forensic evidence subsequently linked him to a series of murders in Czechoslovakia, Austria and the USA

RIGHT Electron micrograph of a human hair root. The DNA information from a single hair found on the seat of a car driven by Unterweger was enough to identify one of his victims

LEFT In Plan de Sanchez, Guatemala, forensic archaeologists examine the contents of a mass grave. The relative position of every bone is carefully recorded so that the cause of death can be accurately determined

BELOW The bones are subsequently examined and accurately measured in the laboratory in order to establish the identity of the skeleton

RIGHT The families of the dead dress the skeletons before the long-awaited traditional burial

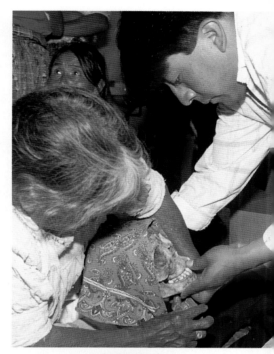

ABOVE The Colombian military destroy opium poppy fields while others (left) carefully harvest the lucrative – and deadly – crop

LEFT Dr Audrey Giles examines a document

BELOW The Tytell family can trace the provenance of a document back to a single typewriter. Each brand, like the Remington (above), has distinguishing features, as does each individual machine

RIGHT Roger Leroy Degarmo on death row. His fate may depend on forensic evidence relating to his sanity at the time of the murder of Kimberley Ann Strickler

INSET Murder witness, John Moers

BELOW PET scans offer the most sophisticated image of the brain currently available to us. They were used in an attempt to prove that Degarmo had suffered brain damage

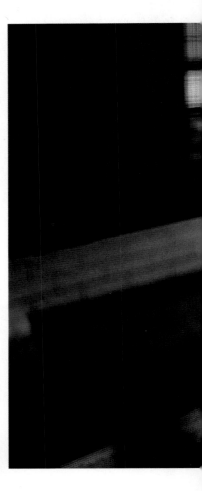

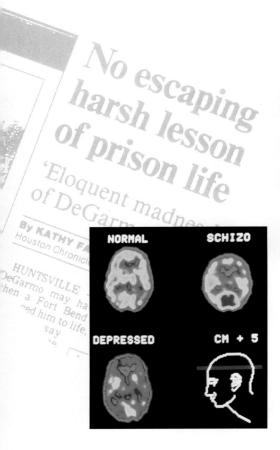

No escaping
harsh lesson
of prison life

'Eloquent madne...
of DeGar...

By KATHY F...
Houston Chronic...

HUNTSVILLE
DeGarmo may ha...
hen a Fort Bend
...ed him to life...
say
...

DeGarmo convicted for 2nd time

Man again found guilty in '79 slaying of Houston wom

By PATTI MUCK
Houston Chronicle

Nearly 15 years to the day after Roger Leroy "Animal" DeGarmo pumped a bullet into the head of a 20-Houston woman, a second

Roger "Animal" DeGarmo was first sentenced to death in 1980, but an

Ann Strickler, was abdu murdered on Jan. 8, 1979.

"I'm thankful for any tims that might have be were turned loose."

The

BELOW Computer image of the DNA double helix. This structure is chemically broken down into segments of different lengths and the process of electrophoresis produces a banded DNA profile (right)

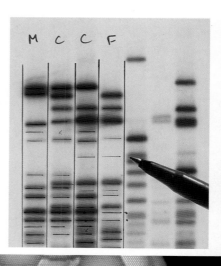

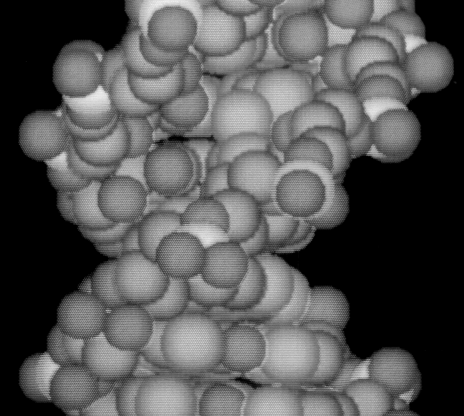

Although Spooner is an expert in the field of cellular telephones, he has been called as an expert witness in court only once. But there are good reasons for that, he insists.

'Normally, as a result of my findings, the defence enters a guilty plea, or they agree to my opinion.'

He is not certified by any governing body, either. 'At the present time, there is no governing organization that offers certification programmes in the field of cellular telephones.'

In the circumstances, it is easy for opposing counsel in a courtroom to play down Spooner's expertise simply by pointing out that: A, he has only ever been called one time as an expert witness, and B, he is not certified by any governing body whatsoever. But Spooner is sanguine about these setbacks and remains energetic in his pursuit of the cellular phone bandits. One of the hardest obstacles to get past, he finds, is apathy.

'Juries in America have a hard time sending someone to prison for this kind of crime, when there are so many murders, so much drug use, and abductions, and beatings, and on and on – stealing telephone numbers doesn't seem like a big deal at all.'

And then there is techno-fear to contend with, or at least techno-resistance.

'People tend to be scared of technology, they don't like to attack it or go after it. Over the last couple of years, though, the US attorneys have been getting much better at understanding the technology, understanding the questions to ask, how the technology works, its vulnerability, and what's needed and what it takes to bring a case to court successfully.'

But public opinion will continue to minimize the seriousness of cellular phone theft, Spooner believes, because the comparative view does not suggest there is any urgent need to impose more severe controls or to upgrade the policing of this branch of white-collar crime.

'The sense of urgency is much greater when a body is found, or if there is a smoking gun. Who really cares if a large corporation lost a couple of million dollars? The general public doesn't really see that as a crime. Unfortunately it's a huge crime, and its ramifications are tremendous. Billions of dollars are being electronically transferred daily across the country, and from this country overseas and vice versa; most of the air-traffic control systems operate over phone lines – thousands of airplanes take off and land worldwide all the time, so heaven forbid the controllers' communications systems should be brought down.'

The speed and ease of cellular-telephone transfer means that more and more individuals and corporations have come to rely on this as a key feature of their operations.

'Electronic transfers are now done over cellular phones,' Spooner says. *'We are now issuing credit reports and mortgage reports to companies over the same air waves. Communication of business proposals and research projects are done with cellular phones – that's all becoming fair game to anyone who can find it, or anyone who can listen in on it. There are security issues involved, integrity issues, personal issues and of course monetary issues.'*

Spooner feels that people must be made more aware. In the meantime, he continues to monitor the activities of the bandits and work towards convictions wherever he can, carefully disregarding the fact that at present, most computer and cellular telephone fraud cases never make it to court.

In spite of the explosive growth in electronic felony, there is no sign of a corresponding decline in the sphere of traditional low-tech white-collar crime. Forgery, one of the oldest recorded misdemeanours, still thrives, although the chances of being caught nowadays are high.

In law, to commit forgery is to make false writing with the intent to defraud which has the effect of prejudicing someone's rights. It isn't limited to business documents.

'Handwriting forgeries were mentioned in Roman law, back in the sixth century,' says Dr Audrey Giles, a forensic document examiner. 'Forgery was rife in Europe, particularly in the churches, in the fifteenth and sixteenth centuries, with the sale of forged papal dispensations.'

Forgery became an offence in England in the fifteenth century. In those days a much smaller proportion of the population could write, so the numbers of people who could engage in forgery were consequently fewer. Even so, a forgery was not nearly so likely to be discovered as it is now.

'Forgers still use a lot of the old techniques,' says Dr Giles, 'which can be dealt with very adequately by the skills of the forensic scientist.'

A document can be any number of things, from a letter, passport or typescript, to a wall with graffiti on it, or a train. On one occasion Dr Giles was asked to examine a tractor destroyed by arson, on which someone had written a message.

'Handwriting has some very important features which give it an advantage over fingerprinting. If you've got a stolen cheque you might find the criminal's fingerprints on it, but that will only prove that he handled it. If you can identify his handwriting on the cheque, that will show he not only handled the cheque, but he actually produced the forged instrument. And that is a crime.'

Forgers, in the main, try to do no more than produce passable copies, and most often the copies they produce are of signatures. Generally they don't worry too much about the shape, structure and proportion of their forgery.

'It's going to be something that is superficially similar to the genuine signature,' says Dr Giles. 'What I look for are the small

details which are missed. They are things like pen-lift in odd places, over-writing, retouching of lines, shaky lines ... The forger is actually drawing the signature, he's not writing it fluently or rapidly in natural penstrokes, so there are features of the signature which will give you a clue that all is not as it should be.'

A forensic document examiner will first of all work out the range of natural variation in strokes and letters in a genuine signature, before examining the suspected forgery. The two are then compared feature by feature. On a typical specimen forgery, Dr Giles noticed a difference in the length of the first stroke of the letter m, and there was a very clear constructional difference in the letter o. Such comparisons, although they call for a sharp and experienced eye, are relatively straightforward. Sometimes the developmental changes in a signature will raise suspicions where none are warranted, and here the document examiner has to be extra-thorough in order to be fair to both sides in the dispute.

'In one particular litigation,' Dr Giles recalls, 'the man defending himself was quite clear that he had signed the questioned documents back in 1988, when he was 18 years old. The principals on the other side of the case looked at the man's present-day signature and those on the documents and decided the signatures were completely different. And they were right. From that they concluded that the man did not sign the 1988 documents. What they didn't do was find the right comparison material. When the case came to me the first thing I did was get on the telephone to Mexico, and ask the man at the centre of the case to search in all his desk drawers and boxes for documents bearing signatures he made in 1988. When several documents turned up it was clear that the signatures were the same as those on the questioned documents. In the years from 1988 to 1994 there had been a huge change in his signature. So, looking only at the 1994 signature was wrong, and it gave the wrong answer.'

Chemical analysis usually means that pieces have to be cut out of questioned documents. Clients don't like having holes made in their papers, and in court an item of evidence is always less than convincing when it has been mutilated, especially if it is the primary offending article in the case. The features that a document examiner usually looks at – the paper, its watermark, staple holes, inks, impressions – can all be studied adequately nowadays using non-destructive techniques.

'I had an inquiry from the solicitors of a public service union,' says Dr Giles, *'because the union were convinced they were losing thousands of pounds through embezzlement by one of their branch secretaries. They were having an enormous amount of trouble pinning this man down as the perpetrator of a fraud, however, because he was able to produce legitimate-looking receipts. I studied each of the receipts for indented impressions using the ESDA technique.'*

ESDA (Electrostatic Detection Apparatus) is a recently developed technique for the detection of indented writing in documents. Before ESDA, it was customary to examine suspected papers with oblique lighting, so that surface irregularities (such as writing impressions) were emphasized and rendered easier to examine. ESDA is far superior. It produces clear, sharp images, and the procedure often reveals marks which are invisible to other methods of examination. ESDA relies on the curious and not completely understood fact that impressions on a sheet of paper cause an alteration in its response to an electrical charge: when a current is applied to the surface of the paper, a charge is set up in the impressions, but not on the flat surrounding area.

ESDA equipment is uncomplicated. It consists of a flat bed made from a porous metal alloy, with a vacuum pump mounted in a box underneath. A roll of Mylar transparent plastic film – like cling film – is mounted at one end of the vacuum bed. Also attached to the unit is a movable instrument called a corona discharge unit. This has a wire inside which can be electrically charged to approximately 8 kilovolts.

The document to be examined is placed on the vacuum bed and covered with a thin sheet of the plastic film. When the vacuum pump is switched on it draws the film into tight contact with the surface of the document – this makes sure the surface is absolutely flat, so that the only irregularities will be indentations in the paper. The corona discharge unit is now passed over the surface of the film two or three times, transferring an electrostatic charge to the plastic. The vacuum bed is next raised at an angle and a cascade developer (a mixture of photocopier toner and tiny glass beads) is poured across the plastic sheet. The toner sticks in any areas of the plastic which are directly over indentations in the paper; applications of developer are continued until the image is dark enough to be read clearly. If the results have to be kept as a record, a sheet of protective adhesive film is laid over the image, producing a permanent transparency. This can then be peeled away from the document, which is left completely undamaged.

'I was handsomely rewarded,' says Dr Giles of her ESDA tests on the suspect receipts. 'Although they were dated over a two-year period, the ESDA results clearly showed that they'd been written out one on top of the other – something which couldn't have happened if they had been issued over a period of years.'

That was not the end of the story. The administrators of the union were interested in expenses claimed for car journeys. A particular diary entry read 'Appointment at St Francis Hospital, Hayward's Heath, Sussex, 11 o'clock'. To the naked eye it looked as if the specimen was all written as a single entry in blue ballpoint-pen ink. Using a high intensity light source to examine the writing, Dr Giles was able to reduce the background luminescence of the paper and at the same time enhance variations of luminescence coming from the ink.

'Because (different) inks are chemically different, they react differently under specialized lighting conditions,' Dr Giles explains. 'The entries "11 o'clock" and "Francis" were absorbing

light strongly, whereas "St" and "Hospital" and the address were fluorescing like mad.'

Another odd thing about the diary was the large number of deletions made with Tipp-Ex, which people do not normally use when they alter their diaries. A special light source was used again to penetrate the Tipp-Ex, showing that crucial times had been altered to tally with a fictitious arrangement of appointments.

'There's no doubt that fraud is on the increase, the crime figures all show that,' Dr Giles says. 'New developments offer new opportunities for forgery or counterfeiting, but forensic science is right behind the forgers and catching up fast.'

In its heyday the typewriter was a huge technological step onward from handwriting. It was nothing less than an epoch maker, and although its use has dwindled with the advent and widespread adoption of word processing, typewriters are still around. Men and women specializing in the investigation of typewriter-related crime are still in business, too.

Along a grimy row of shops and offices in the shadow of Wall Street, through a doorway adjacent to a branch of Radio Shack and one floor up, is the cluttered and overwhelmingly atmospheric office of Martin Tytell, known to lawyers, police officers and newspaper reporters as Mr Typewriter.

The office is stacked to the ceiling with row upon row of typewriters, hundreds of them, representing practically every make and model. Tytell himself fits the scene perfectly, with his shiny professorish dome, his fringe of white hair and a crisp white work coat. He wears a black bow tie, a raffish touch that complements the enthusiasm of his style, the verve with which he describes his work and his consuming passion for the typewriter.

Tytell once fixed President Eisenhower's machine, and Dorothy Parker's. He helped solve the 'Million-Dollar Will' case. He tracked down terrorists who wiped their fingerprints but left telltale signs on typing paper. Mending a machine or tracking down a villain is all part of the job to Martin Tytell. He works with the help of his wife, Pearl, and their son Peter. Pearl, striking in a neat business suit with a long blonde plait wound around her head, is a document examiner. Peter, tidily clipped and bespectacled, is a document examiner and also a history buff; he looks like a dentist sliding into a comfortable middle age.

'If writing was invented on a Tuesday,' he says, 'there was probably a forger working somewhere on Wednesday. It's something that people have done for thousands of years. It can happen spontaneously. Somebody signs something, somebody else notices there's a space left above the signature, so he adds an embarrassing clause. It happens today, and we catch them all the time.'

Martin finds that some anonymous letter writers still work under the delusion that typewriters cannot be identified.

'If you've aligned, as I have, hundreds of machines, a time comes when the machine talks through the marks it leaves on paper. It says I'm an Underwood, I'm a Remington, I'm a Smith, I'm an Olivetti, I'm an Olympia – then I can break it down further, to which model, what year it came out. In some cases I have found myself talking to the typewriter, saying "Did you type this?" and expecting it to talk back to me. In many instances, just one character will tell you the make that you are working with.'

Martin gave an example. The letter m on most machines has three serifs, the small horizontal strokes at the bottom that look like feet. But on one make of machine, one only, there is no central serif.

'The Royal. It's the only machine from which the middle serif is missing.'

Even after a lifetime spent working with them, Martin remains in thrall to typewriters.

'Just think of it,' he says, '2400 parts, put together to do this beautiful thing of creating written work. It's almost human.'

Being a mechanical instrument, the typewriter is subject to wear and tear, and although it will retain certain characteristics which betray its provenance, the longer it is used the more individual it becomes.

'Certain things happen,' Martin says. 'The letters will become defective, the type will not fall into a given baseline – it'll be above the line or below the line. It will slant, it will tilt, it will have other defects. Now all these defects in combination will tell you what you're dealing with, and will tell you that this is a specific machine. It is impossible to take a particular combination of defects and have them occur in another typewriter. Absolutely impossible.'

Most people do not realize the extent to which a piece of their writing is a part of them. Martin knows it only too well; the understanding is part of his stock in trade.

'They can be identified by their idiomatic expressions and by the way they punctuate – punctuation is one of the most basic things that you can zero-in on. And people will type differently – they'll have wide margins, narrow margins, they'll start near the top, and so forth. Given enough material, I can identify the typist.'

Martin quotes a case. 'It had to do with letters, and they were tracked back to a security agency. The administrator told me that this agency had retrained all their typists, so they all would type alike, leaving the same margins, the same headings and so forth. I felt that if I had enough material, somewhere along the line I could identify the typist. After spending several weeks on this, I found that one lady in question had received training at some private school in Switzerland where they taught the typists to leave three spaces after a period, instead of the normal two they taught the ladies here. And sure enough, subconsciously she lapsed into old habits from time to time, and I was able to identify the letters she typed from that irregularity in her typing.'

Pearl mentions a court dispute, in Detroit, over documents which specified the rights of certain members of a family, and these rights operated to the disadvantage of other family members, who had taken the issue to law.

Pearl and Martin were called in to help. They read the suspect documents over and over, looking for any reason to suspect an irregularity in their preparation or content. In the course of one reading Pearl noticed that an 'equals' symbol had been used instead of a hyphen. She and Martin used their knowledge of typewriters to identify the make of machine and the model. Then they took the trouble to check on one thing more.

'So I get a phone call from Detroit,' says their son, Peter, *'asking me to find out when Underwood changed keyboards and put the plus and equals in the top right. I looked through the files and I came back with the date, which was just after the date when the person who was supposed to have signed the document had died. That made it extremely difficult for it to be a genuine document.'*

Then there was the case of the Reverend Sun Myung Moon. He was spiritual leader to millions of followers called the Moonies; he was also alleged to have committed multiple frauds. It was Pearl Tytell who proved beyond reasonable doubt that Moon and his financial associate, Mr Kamiyama, had defrauded the United States Internal Revenue Service.

The disputed documents in the case looked completely genuine to Pearl, but Mr Moon said his signature was a forgery. He said he did not write cheques, and certainly wouldn't write cheques for large amounts to Tiffany's, or certain exclusive and highly expensive antique dealers. But Pearl proved the signatures were genuine.

Financial documents signed by Mr Kamiyama looked genuine, too, but Pearl suspected that the paperwork on Mr Moon's tax documents had been backdated by Kamiyama. Pearl had noticed a watermark on the tax documents, and eventually she tracked it down to a paper mill at Appleton, Wisconsin. Going over the records there, she was able to prove that the paper used in the creation of the tax documents did not exist at the time the documents were supposed to have been dated. To ice the cake, Pearl studied Kamiyama's signature on the tax papers and was able to prove that it was put there two years after he said it was.

The Tytells enjoy their work. They relish the time-consuming, nerve-eroding labour of matching and comparing, backtracking and cross-checking, inspecting and analysing until they find the fake link in an alleged chain of events, or the lie illuminated by something as small as a crooked comma on a typewriter keyboard.

The moment of triumph, when clues fall into place and a case can be proved, is worth all the hard work and the interim failure. *'To make a case is a thrilling thing,'* Martin says, and Peter adds, *'You get the feeling of "Gotcha!"'*

In Washington DC, document examiners are employed full time to limit the damage done to major commercial and financial centres by wholesale forgery and counterfeiting. Those working for the Secret Service are assisted by the only English-speaking version of FISH (Forensic Information System for Handwriting), a new and highly sophisticated computer introduced to make automatic comparisons of handwriting and analyses on forged or disputed bonds. The equipment is also configured to keep a check on the handwriting of letters threatening the life of the President.

Because a single document can carry formidable authority, the need to authenticate with absolute certainty has led to the development of second-rank specialities in the field of document examination. In Washington and London there are sub-specialists in detecting fraudulent photocopies. Occasionally the suspected copies will be skilful composites, pasted and retouched with great care, to create facsimiles of documents that never existed; at other times there will be a whole series of copies alleged to have been made in various places at different dates, but latent marks, such as those from the copier's glass bed, reveal the copies were in fact all made on the same machine, and at the same time.

'We have experts on every aspect of paper fraud,' says the head of a forensic laboratory, 'and the truth is, we need them. There is a lady who knows all about envelopes and whether they've been opened and resealed, and if so, how many times, and how it was done. Another person, an old guy who's been doing it for more than 50 years, can determine the source of the paper in old documents, just by handling them and holding them up to a light, or in some cases cutting off a piece and putting it under a microscope. Mortgage fraud needs the skills of a half a dozen different experts – they have to check paper, handwriting, inks, latent fingerprints ....'

Efforts are made to avoid chemical testing of papers. The process often damages valuable evidence, and in cases where ESDA testing might be an option, prior chemical treatment of any kind destroys a document's potential for this kind of examination. But there are times when chemical tests offer the only hope of finding clues (for example, latent fingerprints) and in such cases fingerprint experts are called in, usually to apply the ninhydrin test. The test is not always successful, but on occasions it produces impressively clear results.

'Ninhydrin is the best method I know of revealing fingerprints on paper,' says a senior fingerprint officer, 'and it's straightforward. Over the years, it's nailed plenty of villains who would otherwise have walked away from the charges against them.'

Papers to be tested are floated on a solution of triketohydrindene hydrate – known in the fingerprinting business as ninhydrin – and gently rocked to and fro, in much the same way that a photographic print is developed. After a short time, if latent fingerprints exist in any strength, they will show up as dark images.

'The method has brought up prints on postal envelopes, currency notes, even betting tickets,' says the head of the laboratory. 'It's just one more way to help us keep up with the bad guys. Like I said, we need all the help we can get.'

Because money is such a uniquely important commodity, most countries treat counterfeiting as a separate crime from forgery, and it carries much higher penalties. New developments in papermaking, ink technology and, most dramatic of all, the accuracy of colour copying machines have made the war against counterfeiters harder to fight and probably impossible to win.

Nevertheless, the agencies set up to combat counterfeiters show no outward despondency. They are prepared to learn all they can about new methods of manufacture and distribution, and they apply their knowledge, often painstakingly and lengthily acquired, to undermining, disrupting and destroying counterfeiting operations in any way they legally can. More doggedly than most, an anti-counterfeit team will stick with a case until it is resolved, even if it takes years of their working lives. To back the specialist investigators in America, where counterfeiting in some regions has hit epidemic proportions, the Secret Service maintains a well-equipped forensics laboratory housing a vast library of counterfeit notes alongside the world's most comprehensive library of inks. They also have a collection of more than 20 000 watermarks which, with the range of inks, is constantly growing.

Although paper crime is still very much a felony of the present, its potential for raising illicit funds is dwarfed by the new international racket known to the police as plastic crime – the hugely profitable trade in counterfeit credit cards.

'I think the same qualities that make Hong Kong a thriving international city,' says Philippe Bertrand, a senior credit card security executive in Hong Kong, 'make some of its residents thriving international criminals. The Tam case is a very good illustration of the phenomenon.'

Between 1989 and the day he wound up at the exclusive Bal Harbour Shipping Mall in January 1993, one man, known as Mr Tam, made a spectacularly swift climb through the developmental and distributive phases of the counterfeit credit card racket.

'Tam was a career criminal,' says Bertrand. 'He had a record that included drug trafficking, and he very quickly learned how to make a success of this new form of criminality. Whether out of hunger or out of luck, he learned, and he learned fast. In 1991 he was trading in re-embossed, re-encoded stolen cards, but by the middle of 1992 he was running his own embossing and encoding facility.'

Tam exploited the local market for his product and, having learned a few things more about the business from the local response, and having encountered pockets of violent resistance and learned how to handle them, he moved on to the softer targets of Europe and Canada in 1991.

'From Canada, of course, it was easy to springboard into the great, vast USA market.'

And the business expanded quickly, because there were high profits to be made for relatively small effort. Tam and his associates got access to legitimate credit cards in criminally backed retail outlets like shops and restaurants; magnetic details were lifted with specially adapted card-swipe apparatus, and very soon afterwards the card numbers would be embossed on genuine-looking blank cards; the matching magnetic information would be encoded on to the track on the back of the card.

The counterfeits were widely distributed. When a fake card was used for a transaction it took about 10 seconds to secure an authorization, but it could be as long as 45 days before the truth came to light and some unsuspecting man or woman learned that a counterfeit – or several counterfeits – of their legitimate credit card had been used to drain their resources.

Ron Morris, the world's leading authority on counterfeit credit cards at the U.S. Secret Service, had an opportunity to examine some of the cards Tam was producing in 1992, and found they were manufactured to practically the same standard as genuine cards.

'They were pretty deceptive,' he admits.

When a card is believed to be counterfeit a forensic expert like Morris studies the hologram, the printing on the card and the embossing, in that order, searching for major discrepancies which usually show up in those areas. He also examines the information magnetically encoded on to the back of the card. Such a detailed inspection would once have produced a sizeable list of differences between a fake and a legitimate card. But not any more. Often an experienced examiner will spend hours with a card, looking for a single sign that it might be a fake. And now the counterfeiters can even duplicate the hologram.

'Holograms were deployed by both Visa and MasterCard from 1982,' says Philip Bertrand. 'That worked until the counterfeiters decided they were no longer going to be deterred by the hologram. They were determined to imitate it. The first attempts, in 1987, 1988, were absolutely horrible looking cards. They had to come up with a better-looking product.'

The incentives were powerful, so Tam and his associates threw themselves energetically into the technological mastery of 'uncopiable' hologram production.

'Since 1989 there must have been ten generations of counterfeit holograms, increasing in quality all the time,' the detective says. 'Now, the production standards have reached a point where an average counterfeit will be good enough to pass for a real one.'

In an effort to keep the technology ahead of the counterfeiters, banks and other finance houses have made the magnetic coding on cards more sophisticated. Now a card can be encoded with not only the account number, but the name of the account holder and the expiry date of the card. There is also a way to check what is known as the bit-density of the encoding – the pattern of dots which make up the individual magnetic characters of the code – to ensure that the information has not been fraudulently applied. On a computer's viewing screen, the pattern of encoding looks like a white silhouette of the Manhattan skyline. If the encoding is counterfeit, the bit-depth analysis will not only detect that, it will also reveal information about the system used to put the code on to the card. If there are variations in pattern from one counterfeit card to another, the investigator knows he is looking for more than one piece of encoding equipment, so possibly he is dealing with cards from two separate counterfeiting establishments, known to investigators as 'finishing houses'.

The plastic used to manufacture counterfeit cards can be microscopically examined to determine its structure. It can also be tested by a process called gas chromatography to determine its composition; this often gives a strong indication of where the plastic came from.

Chromatography is a method of analysis which separates mixtures and substances into their chemical components. The technique depends on the principle of selective absorption (not to be confused with absorption) which is a type of adhesion, or stickiness.

'It still feels like a conjuring trick to me,' an operator says. 'I put in the sample, and by doing hardly anything I can make it give up the secret of its constituent parts.'

Gas chromatography will separate the components of substances that are vaporized by heat. The vaporized material (in this case plastic) is forced by an inert gas along a narrow, coiled tube packed with a porous substance through which the components flow at different rates, depending on their density. In that way they are separated. The substances are gathered at the end of the tube, forming a neat row which amounts to an orderly, visible analysis of the material. The components are noted and can then be checked against a list of formulas supplied by the manufacturers of various types and grades of plastic sheet.

'I could take cards from all over the world,' says Ron Morris, 'and show that those cards were coming out of the same counterfeiting plant. That was rewarding to me, because I knew

I was playing a part in shutting down a major ring of counterfeiters.'

The detection of credit card fraud receives varying degrees of priority with police forces throughout the world. To some analysts, the profits being made are insignificant when they are set beside the recorded earnings from other felonies, and there have been statements – usually from politicians – indicating that too much police time and manpower is expended on this particular branch of crime.

'If you compare credit card fraud to other types of criminality,' says Philip Bertrand in Hong Kong, 'it may sound either enormous, or insignificant. If you compare it to narcotics, $500 billion a year, then the $1.7 billion that was lost because of credit card fraud last year sounds absolutely trivial. If you compare it with the £2 billion or so that was lost by UK retailers because of simple shoplifting, credit card fraud again looks kind of ridiculous.'

But these comparisons, he says, are not valid to anyone looking for a genuinely proportionate evaluation of the profit figures.

'If you compare the figures for credit card fraud with something that is comparable, counterfeit money for example, you get a clearer picture. In a given year, the total amount of all the counterfeit currency that is accounted for, for all the countries in the world, rarely exceeds $200 million. Because currency counterfeiting is taken very, very seriously, across the planet 70 or 80 per cent of the counterfeit money in any given currency is seized before it ever gets into circulation. Today, people who counterfeit credit cards do damage which is, at minimum, eight times larger than the harm done by all the counterfeit currency in the world.'

Ron Morris believes the credit card of the future will be the so-called smart card, a credit card-size piece of plastic with a small computer chip embedded in its surface. The chip's integrated circuit will memorize all transactions for which the card is used, and will maintain a running update of the card-owner's bank account or credit facility balance, or both. Future smart cards would combine all the convenience features of credit cards and direct-debit cards, together with a whole raft of security measures. One device being considered in the United States is a built-in alarm which is activated if the card travels more than a few metres from a tiny sensor worn around the owner's neck. Another device, similar in principle, makes the card inoperative for electronic transactions when it is moved away from its owner. A smart card would also be capable of setting up a 'consumer profile' of the owner, so that if unusual purchases were made with the card, the user would have to provide additional evidence of identity before the transaction could proceed.

Central to all the advances in card design, in card security and card-felony detection, are computers, which have become essential core equipment in the running of Western society. Given that companies large and small rely heavily on these machines, and given the speed, versatility and sheer power of modern computers, it is not surprising that computer crime continues to escalate. This is bonanza territory where even first-time criminals get rich overnight. Computers are everywhere, and their range of capabilities is an invitation to unscrupulous individuals on the lookout for safe ways to make illicit cash.

'If you're going to commit a fraud, large or small,' says a computer fraud investigator, 'it's inevitable that a computer will be involved.'

According to most published studies, the overwhelming majority of computer frauds are committed by authorized users deliberately making false entries at the keyboard. Fraud investigators in various countries have uncovered cases where social services clerks have used computers to authorize emergency payments to clients, who have then split the proceeds with the clerk. An employee in the administrative office of a mail order company used the computer database to produce a list of the 500 best customers and the products they bought most often; he sold the list to the company's major competitor. Every year, workers in personnel departments of large firms invent new employees whose monthly salaries go straight into the fraudsters' bank accounts.

'There is no end to it,' the investigator says. 'Minor crimes like those take place in their millions worldwide, and I don't think they will ever be brought under control. The real worry, as computer systems are relied on more and more for the transfer of funds, is the big-time computer criminal. I'm talking about the man or woman who devises a course of action that will net millions, then sets about doing it the thorough, unhurried way, leaving no clues and occasionally no clear evidence that the money has even been taken.'

Serious computer crime, carried out by experts, means that a person can break into a banking system, steal huge amounts of money, then leave by an electronic 'back door' so that no one even knows they have interfered with the system. In such cases it is often months, sometimes years, before the bank or finance house realizes it has been robbed.

'And of course, there are plenty of organizations who don't want anybody to know they've been robbed,' says the investigator. 'When word gets out that a bank or a building society is vulnerable to computer fraud, it's the worst kind of publicity. It ruins the image of impregnable solidity, and bang goes public confidence and the share values.'

Another reason for not wanting to publicize a major theft is the perfectly justified fear that details of the method used, even if they are presented sketchily in court, will encourage other people to try their hands at computer fraud.

The investigator quotes the case of a female computer operator, working for a New York bank, who heard a radio report of a minor scam uncovered in Kansas, where four field workers for a small charity had altered the sundry daily-expense figures for the entire 120-strong team; they added only a few cents to each individual's total before submitting the regional figures, but they still managed to accumulate enough cash, within two years, to buy each of the four a new car. It was the sudden rash of new cars that had alerted the administrators of the charity, who immediately set up an investigation.

The bank clerk adopted the basic idea of the charity scam and applied it to a fraud of her own. She amended one of the computer programs to add ten cents to every service charge under ten dollars, and a dollar to every service charge over ten dollars. The difference between the official service charge and the charge actually being levied was directed, electronically, into the fictitious account of Miss Harriet Plimpton, an account opened by the programmer herself. For two years she channelled between $700 and $900 every month into the account. She was caught only because the bank one day decided to send circulars to all its customers, and discovered in the process that Miss Harriet Plimpton had no paperwork with the bank; from there it was a short move to the discovery that she did not exist.

'The smallest falsehood can do maximum financial damage,' the investigator says. 'It's all down to knowing how best to abuse the resources at your disposal. George Maguire did no more than change a few addresses, but it made him a fortune.'

Maguire (the name is false) was an insurance agent who altered the addresses in computer records of a number of policies, so that premium notices and other correspondence was sent to his address. He was careful to retype all the bills and important notices and pass them on to the real policy-holders, so that no one was aware that their mail was subject to an unofficial redirect at computer level. George Maguire was able to borrow against the cash value of all the policies. When the insurance company sent the real policy-holders forms to verify the loans, they went to the address on the computer – George Maguire's address. He would always return the forms promptly with the appropriate verification. The scheme, which netted Maguire more than $500 000, fell through when a policy-holder lost the agent's address and called the company to verify the details of his policy. The record of cash borrowing was an immediate cause for noisy complaint from the customer, after which the fraud became increasingly – and embarrassingly – transparent.

'They don't all get caught,' the investigator says. 'A payroll supervisor on a Middle East project set up eight non-existent employees and had their salaries paid into an account of her own by bank transfer. The fraud lasted nine years, until the supervisor left. Nobody heard of her again.'

The business of catching computer bandits seems to rely as much on luck as investigative skill. Computer fraud leaves very few clues and, in cases where the frauds are committed by experts, there is often no incriminating evidence at all.

'Luck tends to improve if you have a rough idea what's going on,' the investigator points out. 'Suspicion on its own is no good as evidence, but if you follow it, you can often wind up with armfuls of evidence – plus, frustratingly, a client who doesn't want to prosecute because of the risk to his image.'

A recent case, where the crime was uncovered by the sheerest luck imaginable, involved a data-input operative who entered false data into a computerized payroll system and netted about $3 million. The scam was an old one, but with the involvement of a computer it stood a much better chance of success than in the old days of hands-on workforce management. The operative and several of his friends became a phantom team of workers who regularly intercepted, endorsed and cashed the payroll cheques made out to their aliases. The fraud was a huge success. No one could say how long it might have gone on, if a police officer had not searched an overdue rental car he found illegally parked, and came across over a hundred of the fraudulent cheques in the glove compartment.

Against such crimes as these, there is practically no forensic defence or possibility of combat, since forensic science relies on the detailed examination of hard evidence, however slight it may be. Computer fraud, when it is restricted to the system itself and the *intangible* deviant intent of an individual or a group, is crime without physical trace. Components in a software system may be tampered with and altered, but they are not engineering parts, they are not solid things at all, so their alteration is usually immaculate and the change carries no clue or echo of what happened or who did it. There are computer defence mechanisms, of course, but anyone with a reasonable knowledge of computer operating systems can usually work around them and, worse, can often use a security system to cover his tracks.

> 'One way we can track what they get up to is when they throw away the evidence of a felony,' says a British investigator of computer crime. 'When a computer is used, say, to overprint a blank driver's licence, or to pass on a fake configuration to a cellular phone, what usually happens is, the person uses a special computer file, or a specially adapted program, to do the dirty work, and when he's finished doing the job, he deletes the file or program from the computer's hard disk. To all intents and purposes it has gone and he's clean, there's no evidence. That's how it looks, anyway, and that's the way it used to be. But not now.'

In recent years the designers of computer software maintenance programs have been steadily refining their file-recovery programs, until they have reached a point of impressively high sensitivity.

> 'In the right hands, a good-quality file-recovery program can find anything lurking in a computer's memory. What happens is, when a file is deleted, it is no longer listed on the machine, it shows no trace of itself, but it is still there. All that's happened is it's been moved from the location where it was labelled and identifiable – it's been de-assigned and can be completely lost

any time the system needs the space the file's occupying.

'Sure enough, after a while, as more programs and files get added to the machine, the deleted files will one by one be lost, they'll slip over the edge of the available free space, or they'll be converted into something else. But if I get hold of a computer soon after a villain has deleted his dirty work – or even a year afterwards, the time doesn't matter as long as nobody has done much work with the machine in the meantime – I can retrieve the files he scrubbed. I can locate them in their now-anonymous state and restore their original identity. I can dig out the little giveaway bits he dumped in the trash and thought he had jettisoned for ever. So that's something, anyway. We don't feel so helpless now that one aspect of computer crime is in our grasp and we can do something about it.'

In recent years a form of guerrilla warfare, the computer virus, has proliferated among business machines, causing havoc and in some cases near-catastrophic losses of data and function. A computer virus is a program specially written to copy itself into legitimate programs and harm computers, usually by slowing down performance or destroying files. With the growth of computer networks, viruses have been introduced either as acts of outright vandalism, or as more subtle devices for financial coercion. One blackmail virus makes its presence known, in the first instance, by freezing the controls of the computer, then putting a message on the screens of all workstations sharing the infected program; the message explains that freeze-ups will keep recurring, without warning and at shorter intervals, and they will stay in effect for progressively longer periods until a certain sum of money is left at a specified spot within a certain period. Failure to comply means the virus will eventually wipe all the files off the computer's memory. If the victims pay up, they will be sent a code which, when entered at the keyboard, will neutralize the virus.

'They get into computers in various ways,' a specialist in virus detection says. 'Usually, it's plain carelessness that gets them on

to a system. If people would just use the lock facility on floppy disks more often, for example, the problem would be cut by half. Viruses can't get on to locked disks. Another way to avoid viruses is to buy software only from legitimate outlets, and make sure the package is factory-sealed when it arrives. Also, there are a lot of shareware programs around, they can be downloaded from electronic bulletin boards, and they're temptingly cheap, but you can't tell where they've been before they get into your machine. One of them could easily be carrying a virus that'll wipe out your files and corrupt your operating system. That could be the most expensive cheap program some people will ever buy.'

Trojan horse viruses are particularly nasty. They appear to be utility programs, such as calendars and electronic reminders, but, when they are run on a machine, a virus hidden within them goes into action, erasing files and doing strange things to the usually logical on-screen functions.

'The most wicked one I ever encountered,' says the specialist, 'was a nice-looking on-screen alarm clock, sent out to a lot of companies as a Christmas present from a stationery company with a name that looked familiar, but turned out to be bogus. The clock program, which was called Al – short for alarm, or so everybody thought – worked just fine the first few weeks, then on 25 January, on the screen of every computer running the program, a message appeared. It said, "You have been selected to be a recipient of Al's revenge" and that was followed by a smaller message at the bottom of the screen – "Palm Island, Florida, 1947".'

People were mystified by the message and they were intrigued to know what kind of revenge had been inflicted on them. The computers appeared to be running normally and, after the message had disappeared from the screens, so had the cute little alarm clock. The program had vanished, and many people were inclined to think the whole thing had been no more than a clever, if puzzling, electronic joke. Then, about an hour after the message appeared, somebody tried to use the printer hooked up to their computer, and discovered the printer password was no longer acceptable.

'Other people tried their printers,' the specialist says, 'and they got the same response – "incorrect password". It dawned quickly after that. The virus called AI had changed all the printer passwords. It had done a good job, too. It was hard to get reliable figures, but we estimated that 400 printers went out of action that day and stayed shut down for a long time, because their internal memories had been manipulated to respond to a new password that nobody knew. In the end it meant equipping the printers with brand-new memory, which wasn't cheap.'

The source of the virus was never uncovered, but it was only a couple of hours before a curious computer operator found out that AI did not stand for alarm.

'It stood for Al, as in Capone. When he came out of prison he was a sick and powerless and prematurely old man at 48. He went to live at a place he owned at Palm Island in Florida, and he died there in 1947.'

The specialist does not see much future in making direct attacks on computer viruses. Their complexity aside, they are often difficult to separate from the legitimate code surrounding them, and the time spent rendering a virus harmless can mean insupportable losses of time and data for smaller companies.

'Viruses are vicious and a lot of them are designed by some sad people purely for recreation. That means, in my view, they can only get more neurotically complex and do more harm as time goes by. Prevention is the best strategy. There is a whole series of good, solid programs that put up warnings if a virus gets into a system, and they can usually destroy it before it gets started up.'

One British university has already lost files because of virus invasion, and another has suffered a serious shutdown and loss of valuable database matter through the activities of hackers.

'Hackers are not such a problem,' says the specialist. 'We can track them nowadays, and smoother chip technology means that a lot of the technical shortcomings they once relied on to cover their tracks don't exist any more.

'But what has really helped in that direction, more than anything, is the fact that so many ex-hackers have turned detective. Suddenly it's an OK thing to do, it's cool, and these guys are very slick because, again, they're enthusiasts, they love what they're doing. They know all the wrinkles and they're tops at guessing the new ones. Tracking down electronic vandals is a challenge to them – one guy says it right out: it's miles better than playing computer games. So one way and the other, criminal hackers don't have such an easy time of it any more.'

Even though big strides are being made against electronic bandits and fraudsters, everyone involved in the forensic investigation of white-collar crime knows that the struggle to contain new avenues of felony gets harder every year. Informed predictions say that soon it will be possible for criminals to make near-perfect counterfeit American dollar bills, extract funds illegally from major banks, manufacture credit cards with perfect holograms and make faultless forgeries of signatures – all from one computer the size of a pocket notebook.

'The basic technology is already there,' says the expert. 'We couldn't stop it being turned to criminal use if we tried.'

There is no doubt that forensic scientists have to struggle to keep abreast of the criminal abuses of technology. They are handicapped by the fact that huge profits and low risks keep criminals determined to bend technology to their own ends. Big rake-offs buy better equipment than the scientists have, and quite often brains are bought, too, or simply hired to create or subvert technology according to need.

'It sounds like science fiction,' says Secret Service agent Mark Spooner, 'but it's not far-fetched. It's very real.'

The war against electronic villainy gets more uneven every day. Beyond a few pockets of strong and perfectly justified hope, there is no sign that forensic science is in any position to win.

the secret

war

A man coming through Heathrow Airport in London is stopped by customs officers and his luggage is searched. Among the clothing and other personal items, the officers find a photograph album filled with snapshots. The album pages have not been properly attached to the binding; the finish of the whole product has an amateur appearance and, as a commercial product, it feels wrong. The album is confiscated and the man is taken to a high-security room where he remains in detention while his suspect item of luggage is examined.

The album is taken to a specialized laboratory where a team of technicians, working under the supervision of government chemists, cut the pages into very small pieces. These are experienced people who are not easy to fool. Within a short time, using chemical separation procedures especially developed for this kind of work, they have extracted a fine white powder from the pages of the album. The powder is pure heroin, which will be entered in the record as diacetylmorphine. The courier of the drug, still in detention at the airport, is charged with importing an illegal substance under the Drug Trafficking Offences Act. It is almost certain he will be given a heavy jail sentence.

*'For every one of the couriers they catch,' says a US journalist,
'10 or 11 will get through. Sheer weight of product wins the day.
This stuff is cheap to make, remember – it's only really expensive
to the poor sucker who buys it so he can shortcut the
destruction of his health.*

*'If you look at the picture without shading your eyes, you can't
escape the conclusion that the moral fabric of the world is
crumbling under the pressure of drugs. That may sound
melodramatic, but you only have to get close to the people
dealing in drugs to see fanaticism running at full blast. Those
guys are grimly single-minded. And they don't intend to be
stopped.'*

Bangladesh, a country of 115 million people, is believed to have
1.3 million drug addicts, even though the Parliament has enacted a
law providing the death penalty for anyone trafficking more than 25
grams (less than an ounce) of any dangerous drug.

*'Profit is the magic word of our time,' says the journalist. 'Even
some of the little people in the drug manufacturing chain can
make serious money, and certainly when you get close to the
finished saleable product, you're talking about profit that runs
into several hundred per cent.'*

The production of cocaine, a drug which has accelerated the
rate of addiction worldwide, has become a jealously protected
source of livelihood for thousands of people who would otherwise
possess nothing.

*'I've been to Bolivia,' the journalist says, 'and I've seen the
farmers, more than four thousand of them at one time, try to tear
policemen and DEA officers to death with their bare hands, all
because the government tried to clamp down on the country's
exports of coca. The farmers seized the police barracks in Villa
Tunove in the Chaparé Province, which is where most of the
Bolivian crop is grown. Five farmers died in the fighting. It was
like civil war, and in a lot of ways that's what it's turned into, with*

the government on one side trying to hammer the cocaine trade and the violent crime that goes with it, and the drug industry workers on the other side, defending their livelihood to the death.'

People make drugs because the return on investment in time and raw materials is probably the highest for any manufacturing process in the world. Further along the chain other people sell drugs because the product is of proven commercial viability; the market, once established, is prone to growth, and the profits are sometimes unbelievably high. People who buy the product do so because taking drugs makes them feel better than any other activity accessible to them. Some drugs produce tranquillity of a kind impossible to imagine; others induce incredible elation and levels of apparent self-awareness that would be unattainable by any other means. These states do not persist, of course, but by the time a drug has become more of a chemical dependency than a passport to nirvana, the user has to keep on buying, however bleak his disillusionment.

It all started a long time ago. Opium is thought to have been discovered in the Neolithic Age; Hippocrates appears to have used it for medicinal purposes, and so did Galen. The rest of the world was introduced to opium by Turkish traders in the ninth century. By the sixteenth century it was a trade commodity of European mercantilists; at one point opium provided half the revenue of certain colonial administrations. Most Asian cities had opium dens controlled by European governments. The objections of one Chinese emperor sparked the first Opium War (1839–42), which the Europeans, technically the pushers, won. American 'china clipper' ships, which were known to the trade as 'opium clippers', had a large quota of this trade.

Morphine was first derived from opium in 1806 by the German chemist F. W. A. Sertürner. It was a superb analgesic, even relieving the pain of certain soft-tissue cancers, but widespread medical use of the drug produced problems, mainly a tendency towards addiction. Codeine, a further derivative, was also found to be addictive. In 1874 yet another derivative, called heroin, was developed, and at the time it was believed to be a non-addictive wonder drug. Cocaine, isolated from coca in 1858 but not used medically until 1888, was at first considered to be a cure for morphine addiction, and when the first soda fountains appeared in America in 1892 cocaine was a popular ingredient of tonic drinks, Coca-Cola among them. The drug was excluded from soft drinks by the Pure Food and Drug Laws of 1906. Inventors of patent medicines did a solid trade, particularly in isolated communities, selling powerfully addictive 'tonics' and stamina-builders such as Sydenham's Syrup and Godfrey's Cordial. These products were used so widely that by 1902 an estimated one million Americans, mostly women, were addicted users of opiates.

The relatively unrestricted distribution of narcotic drugs by doctors and pharmaceutical companies created a drug-abuse problem on a gigantic scale. In the early 1920s, federal authorities estimated there were 200 000 addicts in America. At this time measures were taken to stem the flow of opium from the Near and Far East.

By a multi-stranded process similar to that underlying the concentration of crime in certain quarters, narcotics use in the early twentieth century tended to gravitate to metropolitan slums and lower-working-class areas. But nowadays, as sharper commercial minds have turned to the marketing possibilities of a high-profit product that guarantees customer loyalty, the use of narcotics has spread to middle-class youth. In reaction, the middle class now regards narcotic addiction as a psychological problem. Previously, when drug addiction was the exclusive province of the slum people, it was a police problem.

The Latin American connection
Latin America is the world's largest producer of cocaine, and turns out significant quantities of marijuana and heroin. Most of the coca leaf which is eventually converted into cocaine is grown in Bolivia

and Peru. Since the early 1970s Colombia has been the main refiner and exporter of cocaine; by the 1980s it was also the third largest cultivator of the coca plant. Between them, the Colombian and other Latin American drug cartels now export approximately 250 tons of cocaine a year to the United States.

The marijuana smoked in America mainly originates from Latin America and the Caribbean, most of it from Mexico and Colombia, with lesser amounts trickling in from Jamaica and Belize. Mexico also turns out most of the heroin used in the USA. In recent times, Brazil has been emerging as an energetic competitor in the drug-export business, and it may soon enter the main league. Almost every country in Latin America serves as a distribution point for drugs and, increasingly, all of these countries have become heavy consumers of the product they help to peddle.

If drugs were legalized, Latin America would have very little competitive edge. Marijuana and heroin can be grown anywhere, and the trade in cocaine would resemble international trade in any ordinary home-grown product. However, as long as the drugs remain illegal, and as long as the demand grows, the dollars will continue to travel south in their millions every year.

The illegality of drugs has been the governing factor in pricing policies – the thing is forbidden, but you want it badly, so you can have it if you pay a lot for the privilege of having what is forbidden.

'It reminds me of the Lady Chatterley case,' says a British researcher. 'People used to pay all kinds of silly prices for a copy while the book was a banned title. As soon as it became available openly – which for a start took away a lot of the mystique – you couldn't find anybody who had managed to read it all the way to the end. When it was stripped of the forbidden tag and made freely available, the book shrank to its true proportions and people largely ignored it from then on.

'The legislators are sustaining that kind of phoney mystique on the drug scene. If they said, "Oh to hell with it, go ahead and peddle the stuff", the number of users would drop by near enough a half straight away. The sexy "forbidden" tag would be

gone and only the hard-core druggies would remain. Which is OK, since there's no hope for the poor bastards anyway.'

People in Latin America who once subsisted on meagre legitimate incomes now live rather well; they include families who farm coca, the marijuana growers of Mexico, Colombia, Jamaica and Belize, and the many thousands in Mexico involved in the cultivation and harvesting of opium poppies. Corrupt politicians and police officers also benefit from the trade and unspecified amounts are pumped into unofficial health and welfare programmes for the manual workers.

Uplifting tales of success are abundant. In the early 1980s Juan Jiminez and his family lived in a house made from canes, rushes and sun-baked clay. Juan, an old man before his time, worked as a gardener to a wealthy Colombian coca farmer. Most coca farmers do well, but this one did better than most, because he had had the sense in the early 1950s to lay claim to acres and acres of undeveloped land and then, by the sweat of his brow, clear it and plant it and keep it cultivated. Then he waited for ten years, convinced of the coming bonanza predicted by an American who had sold the farmer his first refrigerator. Waiting paid off and his gigantic annual crop became the subject of much bidding and counter-bidding. The farmer became a millionaire.

One day the farmer's brother, who also managed the farmer's staff and looked after his cars, came to Juan's house and asked if his son, Pascuale, was old enough yet to read. The boy was in fact 12 and he could read very well, and he could do mathematics and work out basic problems in physics, thanks to the diligence of his mother, who had saved to have him taught by French nuns. The farmer's brother was pleased; he had a letter which neither he nor the farmer could understand, but it looked very important, too important to ignore. It transpired, some time later, that the reason they could not understand the letter, or any letter, was that neither the farmer nor his brother could read a word.

Pascuale read the letter, which requested the farmer to make available samples of his three main crop strains for collection by a chemist who would be calling later that week. The brother thanked Pascuale, gave him a coin, and went away. Ten days later he returned and asked the boy to read another letter. This one told the farmer that the chemist had decided he would set up a laboratory at the farm, which was truly vast, so that crop quality-control could be managed at source and the various different leaves assigned correctly for specific manufacturing destinations.

Although people as lofty as the farmer's brother did not usually stoop to engage in conversation with the likes of Juan Jiminez, on this occasion the brother did admit to the gardener that the business was getting too complicated now that it was organized on such a scale. 'Too much paper work,' he said. 'Too much call for reading and writing.'

In the space of a month the young Pascuale was virtually a permanent installation at the farmer's mansion, reading letters, writing others, and making out lists dictated by the chemist. For being so useful Pascuale was rewarded with a regular wage, almost three times what his father earned, and the family were rehoused in a real cottage much nearer the mansion.

At the end of the chemist's two-month stay, he approached Juan Jiminez and his wife and asked them if they would like their son to train to be a chemist. The boy showed great aptitude, the chemist said, and such young men could prosper in today's business world. Juan and his wife gave their permission, and Pascuale went away to Barranquilla to learn to be a drug chemist.

It took three years. In that time Pascuale learned how to use solvents to extract the essence from leaves and then refine the essence into a powder which had then to be refined still further and appropriately diluted with dried gum and corn starches. He also learned the principles of stock control, laboratory management and the evaluation of crops.

After his first year he showed such a capacity for learning, and for keeping quiet, that he was taken to Mexico where he met an American senator and rich Mexicans and Colombians who had an interest in supplying Pascuale's master with all the resources he needed to keep his work running smoothly. Pascuale learned that the master had trained more than a dozen other chemists, all of them working on their own initiative throughout Colombia, Mexico and Peru, and being paid more in a week than Pascuale's mother and father between them earned in a year. Pascuale came to understand there were bonuses, too – women, cars, travel. All the chemists needed to give in return was their skill, their loyalty (which amounted to no more than silence) and the firm promise never, ever to let one particle of any drug enter their bodies.

In the third year of his training Pascuale was ambushed one night in the town of Bucaramanga; the men who seized him took him in a car to a hotel where they tied him up and threatened him with a knife, saying they would cut off his *cojones* and stuff them in his mouth if he did not tell them where the master kept the central supplies of chemicals used for refining the cocaine.

The ordeal lasted more than two hours, and throughout it all Pascuale spoke not a word. He was finally taken out of the hotel, put in the car again, then driven into the edge of a forest and thrown out. He never saw the men again, he never talked about his ordeal to anyone, yet the master knew all about it. He told Pascuale how pleased he was with him, and how his loyalty and his silence would forever pay dividends.

Today Pascuale is in his mid twenties. He runs four major laboratories and has control of more than a hundred lab workers. He is rich, with three homes, two cars and a couple of live-in girlfriends. His mother and father now live in some style in a beautiful villa in San Felipe; the place is gaudily furnished and pride of place goes to an oil portrait of Pascuale, mounted on an easel in the hallway. Juan always tells visitors, whether or not they actually ask, that the handsome fellow in the painting is his son Pascuale, who made himself and his family rich by dedicating his life to science.

There is no way to know for certain how much the Latin American drug market is worth. An estimate from the Bolivian government suggests that cocaine exports put an annual $700 million into the economy, which is much higher than the figure for all its legitimate exports added together. The figure for Peru is probably about the same. Colombia has structured its involvement in the international drug scene rather differently from the others: it grows much less coca than Bolivia or Peru, but it converts much of their production into the finished product, ready for marketing, and therefore earns a huge annual processing fee. The most recent attempt at an overview was made by a group of former US government drug-control officials. These men and women are now engaged upon a privately funded project, establishing a tactical world map of drug production and routes of distribution, with a view to setting up active international resistance at every strategic point.

'Their figure stands a better chance of being accurate than anybody else's,' says a spokesman, 'and that includes the government's own figures. The estimate, based on trafficking information picked up in the United States and in Latin America, is $2.5 billion per annum. Tax free, of course.'

The uncorrupted quarters of the various Latin American governments are despondent about the chances of finding a way to resolve their drug problems. Income produced by the drug trade would not be replaceable from any legitimate source if the trade were stopped. Millions of lives may be destroyed by drugs, but that argument cuts no ice with a man or woman whose comfortable way of life is a direct consequence of the existence of an illegal drug trade.

War against the traffickers, long thought to be the ultimate weapon once it was properly applied, is now known to have little effect. The traffickers have a lot of space to run and hide in, their crops are too big and too numerous to be attacked on anything like a harmful scale, and their processing plants can be taken down and moved from one location to another in a matter of hours.

'It has been said there are maybe two hopes for Latin America's drug headache,' an observer says. 'One is a really huge drop in the world demand for cocaine, the other is legalization of the drug. It's like saying the cure for these hamburger joints all over the world is for everybody to turn vegetarian. It's not going to happen, is it?'

Since most cocaine comes from Latin America, it is relatively easy to target the source and try at least to inhibit the supply. Heroin is different. There are a number of producer countries, so in order to monitor the rate of output from one country and another, it is necessary to detect the identity of seized consignments. That job is part of the work of the Drug Enforcement Administration, the DEA.

The DEA is an agency of the US Department of Justice and was established in 1973 as a unit to merge the functions of four separate drug law enforcement agencies. The main stated task of the agency is to reduce the supply of illicit drugs produced domestically or entering the USA from abroad. They also have a role in regulating the legal trade in narcotic and dangerous drugs. They operate a nationwide narcotics intelligence system, and work in concert with other agencies to try and suppress the internal drug traffic. In 1982, the Federal Bureau of Investigation and DEA were granted dual jurisdiction over drug offences. Agents of the two organizations now work together on drug law enforcement, and the administrator of the DEA reports to the director of the FBI. In addition to a nationwide network of offices in America, the DEA has offices in more than 40 foreign countries.

Ben Perillo is in charge of the special drug testing laboratories of the DEA, where they have developed a number of highly sophisticated techniques for identifying the source of drugs by making the drug samples 'talk'. Perillo says it was rather like an interrogation. Each drug sample speaks eloquently and can provide a lot of information, but a way has to be found to translate the particular language of a given sample.

Depending on the process used to manufacture the heroin, it will contain certain chemical traces. These can be detected by mass spectrometry, which is a complex way of spreading out the components of a substance visibly, so that its particular chemical identity can be profiled in precise detail. By this means the DEA's experts can usually tell where a sample of heroin has come from.

From profiling and drug seizures in various countries it is now known that there are three drug 'signatures' which correspond to the three main areas of heroin production. The first is the South East connection, known as the Golden Triangle, which takes in Burma, Thailand and China. Then there is the Golden Crescent, made up of Afghanistan and a number of neighbouring countries. Most European heroin comes from these sources. The third and least significant source, in terms of actual quantities imported, is Mexico.

Ben Perillo explained that there are constant efforts by traffickers to suppress signs of a heroin consignment's country of origin. The Mexican heroin normally has a distinctive tint, but they try to confuse the DEA by whitening it. Again, a check of the chemical make-up of the drug will usually assert its identity. The results of these checks over the years have often quite incidentally shown huge swings in the patterns of importation. Until 1988 the bulk of heroin reaching the USA came from Afghanistan; then there was an abrupt switch to product from the Golden Triangle, an indication that the Chinese gangs importing Eastern heroin were attempting to take over the markets.

'Science which accurately targets the source of drugs is a tool beyond price,' says a specialist observer. 'You can be all over the place, trying to stop the stuff coming in, and probably catching only a tiny fraction. On the other hand, if you know there are big output pushes going on in certain parts of the world, there's enough international police co-operation to put a crimp in the export plans of whatever organization is currently trying for the upper hand.'

From time to time even the experts are fooled. A shipment of powder from Colombia, confiscated from a ship stopped at Miami, was assumed to be cocaine, since that is Colombia's most notable powdered white export. But on examination it was found to be heroin, with many of the features of the product traditionally exported from Afghanistan.

The DEA did not want to believe that there was a new strain of heroin being manufactured in Colombia. Intelligence had indicated no such production. At the time of the discovery, Ben Perillo reasoned that the Colombian cartels had employed a chemist from Afghanistan to work for them, enabling them to diversify their line of products. Top brass at the DEA did not accept even the likelihood that Perillo's guesswork, however astute, could be right. They reasoned that the sample must have come from somewhere else.

However, a drug bust inside Colombia a year later uncovered substantial stocks of locally produced heroin with a chemical 'signature' that made it look like Afghanistan product. Perillo's speculation had been correct.

'And all the time these raids and busts are going on,' says the American journalist, *'the same old question is being asked, right up at the top where the moves are planned: how do we stop the trade? What size of strike will it take to curb the flow of poison into the veins of Western civilization? And the answer, the quick one, is that it can't be done. The really practical observers say it's not even worth trying.'*

The record bears this out. The DEA's war on imported cocaine was a dismal failure. Burning the Colombian cocaine fields and staging military attacks against the barons did no more than heighten the enmity and the risks associated with trafficking. It did not stop the flow. Because of all the trouble, the barons and 'shifters' decided to insert a hardship levy in their pricing strategies, which the consumers paid without resistance. So the net outcome of punitive action against the barons was that their profits were increased by anything up to 20 per cent; sales figures rose, too, as people bought more than they needed, because rumours about a shortage created by military action against the producers set off a spate of panic buying.

In Britain and Europe, the price of cocaine began to drop in the late 1980s as saturation in the American market meant the traffickers had to spread their sales effort wider.

'Easy availability and reduced charges meant we were getting new addicts at the rate of dozens a week,' says an official of the Jude Trust, which monitors drug use in major British towns and cities. 'Quite a few people died, some became permanently psychotic, and many, many were plunged into a lifestyle that cost more than they earned.'

The price of addiction

For those with a habit that costs more than they can earn, the traffickers themselves sometimes offer an answer. Geraldine, a Londoner, was 19 when she became addicted to cocaine, and was swiftly moved along, by her pusher, to the even deeper miseries of crack. On the day Geraldine approached the pusher and began begging for a fix, he rightly deduced that this was one addict who could not successfully turn to stealing to pay for the habit. It was probably something other than compassion that prompted the pusher to recruit Geraldine as a go-between.

'It happens a lot in the cities, the go-between lark,' says a police officer. 'The pusher is known to the punters, and from the pusher's point of view that's good, because he doesn't have to do much to attract the custom – old punters know him, and new ones are pointed in the right direction by the established ones. But the police get to know the pushers, too. So what happens is, the pusher handles the cash element of the transaction, but he won't run the risk any longer of getting caught with drugs on him. So the punter has to hang around until someone unknown to him comes by and puts the drugs into his hand. That's the go-between, the poor soul who will sooner or later get done for

handling. The go-between is usually an addict who does the job for the price of a fix.'

Geraldine soon found it impossible to concentrate on her job in a mini-market; her ability to focus on a line of action for more than a few minutes was gone, along with her ability to maintain a calm front. She began making customers nervous with her twitchy movements, her habit of losing the drift halfway through answering a question, and her new, unwitting practice of whining softly when she breathed. She was fired and had to claim unemployment benefit, a prospect which terrified her. She went to her pusher and used some of her severance pay to buy herself a fix, something to calm her nerves when she went to the Social Security office.

At the office, she experienced what is known to drug therapists as a rebound episode – not to be confused with drug flashbacks, which are different – and it happened while Geraldine was making her claim. All at once she was seized by a sense of impending disaster and a certainty that she would suffocate if she remained in the office. Before anyone could stop her she had clambered on to the window ledge and stepped out through the open window. She fell three storeys to the street and broke both legs.

While she was in hospital, suffering hideous pain from her multiple fractures, and acute withdrawal from crack, she was visited by the pusher. In an open ward, he offered to inject her with morphine to kill the pain and take her away from her misery for a day or so.

'No one can begin to fathom these weird acts of misguided compassion in the chemical kingdom,' says a drug counsellor. 'They happen, and they can be so bizarre – one woman on my books, a chronic depressive, was asked if she would like to have a baby to look after, one she could keep if she wanted. The pusher believed a baby would cheer her up and he knew where he could easily steal one, any time he liked. My patient refused, of course, even when he assured her it would be no trouble.'

Geraldine accepted the offer of the morphine. The shot was administered in such a way that no one saw what was happening, and Geraldine soon passed out. Unfortunately her level of unconsciousness kept dropping until she was in coma and her breathing began to falter. She was only just saved when an alert nurse noticed what was happening and called a resuscitation team.

It was a month before Geraldine got out of hospital, and even then she had to walk with the aid of sticks. She had been back at her bedsitter only a few minutes when the pusher showed up and told her how she could earn a few pounds and a decent fix. This presented Geraldine with a dilemma: she had finally and painfully passed through the symptoms of withdrawal while she lay in hospital, and she did not really want to touch crack again. On the other hand, she was badly depressed and had spent that entire morning wondering just what she would do with herself back out in the world again. So she agreed to do the job and was given an advance payment of cash, plus a small envelope of crack.

At eight o'clock that evening, acting on the instructions of her pusher, she went to a cinema in the West End of London and stood near the entrance, waiting for a man with a white scarf to stop and ask her if she was Gerry. When he said that, all she had to do was hand him the folded newspaper the pusher had left with her. She knew from past dealings that the newspaper probably had packets of crack glued between its pages.

The encounter turned out to be more eventful than Geraldine had expected. As the man spoke to her and took the paper, three other men closed in; two of them grabbed the man, the third took hold of Geraldine. They were drug squad officers, and back at the station Geraldine was encouraged to tell as much as she knew about her pusher. She was very frightened and gave a complete description of the man, who was eventually picked up, questioned, then let go for lack of material evidence.

When eventually Geraldine was released, later that same night, the pusher met her on the street where she lived. He explained to her that her life was relatively easy – all she had to do was submit and keep her mouth shut, there was really no more to it than that. But she had gone and rocked the boat. She had seen fit to inform on him, which she was bound to have known would do him no harm, it would merely get him agitated, which was what the police liked to do to him from time to time. So, on account of the agitation, he said, Geraldine owed him. Before she could ask him how she could square the debt, he had taken one of her sticks from her and pushed her over. She fell awkwardly, breaking her leg again, and as she lay on the pavement gasping for enough air to scream with, the pusher beat her savagely with the stick, cracking the bones of her face and knocking an eye completely from its socket. One blow too many on her head finally knocked Geraldine unconscious.

Sixteen months later, when Geraldine had been rehabilitated and had a job in the kitchen of a health farm in Sussex, an officer of the charitable trust which had rescued her sent a brief letter of thanks to an orthopaedic surgeon at the Middlesex Hospital, who had saved Geraldine's leg. The officer's letter ended as follows:

In her short life Geraldine has known more suffering and despair than most of us could ever imagine, and every shred of the blame can be laid at the door of drug dependence. Drugs first took her health, then her pride, most of her dignity and finally they nearly exacted the price of her life. As matters stand she has only one eye and she is a partial cripple, and she has just turned 21. It is an awful story, but we thank you again for helping its outcome to be far less terrible than it might have been.

Prices of cocaine in the UK gradually rose to previous levels and beyond as the market was established and entered a phase of steady growth. But changes were still occurring, making the marketplace volatile, making it amazingly profitable and extremely dangerous for rival traffickers. With the collapse of the Berlin Wall the Eastern approaches were freed up and suddenly there was a wide open road across Europe for heroin from Afghanistan.

'And around that time the whole culture of the designer drug seemed to explode,' says the official from the Jude Trust. 'They were called designer drugs because, unlike the stuff people had abused in quantity before, they weren't made from natural substances. They were completely synthetic. These were compounds of other chemicals, and the other chemicals were freely available in the marketplace. It was quite a phenomenon, a trade in illegal substances that were made from legal components.'

This category of drugs was also labelled 'recreational', giving the impression that they were adornments of the lifestyle, rather than harmful and in many cases life-threatening toxic agents. This was the onset of a chemical drug revolution which mirrored the 1960s' philosophy of 'living through chemistry'. The market for the new drugs, however, was almost exclusively teenage.

A psychiatrist specializing in drug-related psychoses and other disturbances attributable to drugs observed not only an expansion of the regular drug-taking scene, but a clear social division.

'The people who usually get labelled addicts, the heroin junkies and users of strong amphetamines, tend to be regarded by the synthetic drug users as a sub-class, a band of hopeless addicts. Cocaine users have a tendency to frown on the heroin addicts as well, even though their own addiction is just as dominant and potentially as harmful. Young people, in the main, aspire to the designer drugs and the outlook which goes with them – a belief that they are already sharp individuals and the drugs merely add an extra fine edge. I've even had a patient say that she thought some people were wasting their time taking Ecstasy and MDA because they were dummies, and the drugs did nothing for dummies except make them dumber.'

The designer products
There is no such thing as a comprehensive list of designer drugs,

because new items float on and off the market all the time. Since the manufacturing process is not regulated, many drugs with new names are simply old ones revamped, sometimes only in name alone; others are not drugs at all but simple placebos, sometimes flavoured talc in tablet form. The information in the abbreviated list which follows is derived from sources close to the current recreational drug scene in Britain and the United States.

MDMA (Ecstasy)

The drug's chemical name is enshrined in a number of pharmacological texts: it is 3,4-methylenedioxymethamphetamine, a semi-synthetic compound which was first synthesized in 1914 as an appetite suppressant. It was found to have 'undesirable' side-effects, so the manufacturers did not market the drug and they let the patent lapse. The drug reappeared in the 1960s with other psychoactive substances. Since its second re-introduction in the 1980s MDMA, or Ecstasy, has been the most popular drug of abuse among people in the age range 15 to 25.

One user, knowledgeable about pharmacology, disagrees with the labelling of this class of substance as a designer drug. 'Designer drugs are dangerous narcotics,' he says, 'MMMP is an example, it's a synthetic heroin with an impurity that causes Parkinson's disease. The new psychedelics, like Ecstasy, are made from a crossing of a mescaline-style structure with amphetamine – speed. There are hundreds of these chemical bondings, and many of them seem to be safe psychedelics when they're properly used.'

In the *San Francisco Chronicle* of 10 December 1987, David Perlman quoted a psychiatrist who had recently tried Ecstasy for the first time and said, 'It may be the first pharmacological agent that gives a patient the capacity for insight. It enhances positive feelings of love and trust and seems to facilitate the retrieval of early memories.'

In low doses (100 mg is regarded as normal) Ecstasy is said to have mild effects, rather like low doses of LSD and speed, but with no hallucinations. Despite its relatively gentle effects in minor dosage, however, it can leave the user with a hangover-like headache for up to two days. High doses result in LSD-type trips and can cause sickness.

MDMA, or Ecstasy, or E as it is now more commonly called, is a popular accompaniment to dance music in spite of its cost – around £15 for 100 mg – and despite (or maybe because of) adverse publicity in the press. In Amsterdam in 1989 the police seized 900 000 tablets of Ecstasy; the following year 5500 tablets were seized in London. In 1991, another bust in London resulted in the seizure of 66 200, which indicates a steady increase in European supplies.

There is a confusion between MDMA and MDA, which is a much more powerful drug and is actually substituted for MDMA by peddlers unable to obtain supplies of Ecstasy. MDA has serious, occasionally fatal, side-effects even in low doses. There have been a few reported deaths from the use of Ecstasy, too, but in spite of that there are an estimated half million users of Ecstasy in the UK.

DOB ('Bromo-STP')

This drug circulated in Britain in 1973 and has resurfaced at various times since. It is a stronger version of the 1960s drug DOM (or STP), which was then sold as a substitute for LSD. Usually DOB is sold as drops on blotting paper, like LSD, because it is very potent in any but the tiniest quantity.

In recent times producers have been selling DOB in massive overdosages which produce hallucinogenic effects lasting as long as 36 hours. The drug apparently does not suit everyone but has a fairly large and loyal following.

E4Euh (Intellex)

A long-lasting (14 hours average) amphetamine derivative. It is claimed that it improves intelligence temporarily and encourages verbosity; some of the effects are like those of MDMA. Mixes very badly with LSD.

DM; DET; DP; DIPT

These are all chemically related to psilocin, which in turn is derived from psilocybin, a hallucinogen which can be obtained from the mushroom *Psilocybe mexicana*. The first three have no action when they are taken orally, and have to be smoked – but not with tobacco, which can produce a highly toxic interaction. They have short-lasting but intense LSD-type effects. DIPT is orally active and is claimed to be so specific in its action that it only alters the perception of music.

Smart drugs

There are a number of materials reputed to have improving effects on mental functioning and memory. They range from vitamin supplements and nutrients available in health shops, to patent medicines sold through mail-order outlets. The 'Emperor's New Clothes' syndrome seems to operate in this area, with few people being prepared to say they find an underground fashion lacking in effect. Whatever the case, the smart drugs are all legal and most are probably lacking in any ability to modify brain activity.

With the onslaught of synthetic drugs, the authorities realized it was pointless to target traffickers alone. There was an extra element, a supply network of precursors, the chemicals (many of them legal in themselves) which go towards making drugs such as Ecstasy.

'It was a case of identifying the chemicals first,' says a chemist engaged on investigations of designer drugs. 'Then they had to find out where each was made.'

The manufacturing processes involved in making most drugs are known to chemists and, when a list of the most frequently used precursors had been assembled, it was found that they no longer emanated from just a few manufacturing outlets, as previously. Now, they were being made in tin huts and disused warehouses and all manner of derelict buildings in up to eight or nine different countries. As the illicit drug trade had changed, so had the manufacture and distribution of precursors.

'When you're dealing with something like MDMA,' says the chemist, 'the precursors are highly identifiable substances like safrole, isosafrole, piperanol and so forth, which at one time we could pinpoint and say, well, you'll find that being manufactured in such and such a place. But not now. The fact was, some of the places where precursors had traditionally been manufactured were now likely to be the last places you'd find them.'

And some drugs provided chemical breakdowns that were of no use in detecting a source. 'That's usually because they're manufactured right under our noses,' the chemist says. 'Like crack. Now that's an almost pure form of cocaine, and if you analyse the crack crystals, you may find traces of ammonia and baking powder – but if you do, so what?'

Crack is made in home laboratories by preparing a solution of cocaine hydrochloride in water, to which ammonia, with or without baking powder, is added. This draws out the alkaloidal form of cocaine, which is the part the addicts smoke. From the standpoint of distribution crack is unique, because it has never had to be imported. Only the cocaine comes from abroad, in convenient powder form, for the home chemist to convert to the highly addictive crack 'rocks', which sell for much more, gram for gram, than straight cocaine.

'When it was found that the precursors were being manufactured all over the place, by chemists whose whole professional existence was dedicated to the illicit drug trade,' says the chemist, 'the only answer seemed to be to organize legislation that would declare the precursors illegal, and make their import an offence.'

In 1988, an international agreement was drawn up, controlling the manufacture and movement of 18 chemical substances known to be used as precursors in the manufacture of illegal drugs.

'And in 1994, after all the signing and agreeing and the demonstrations of international solidarity in the face of the drug menace, guess what? The trade still goes from strength to strength, and there's no shortage of precursors.'

The legislation did hamper and in some cases stop the manufacture of certain precursors, but the drug chemists (known as 'covert chemists') simply found alternatives, or devised them. A whole new phalanx of precursors grew up, all of them perfectly legal and therefore freely transportable from country to country. The continuing profiling of synthetic drugs, according to Howard Stead, a UN adviser on precursors, showed that when a chemist could not obtain a particular precursor, he simply took a step back or sideways in the manufacturing process and used a chemical that was not proscribed by legislation. It is a game of cat and mouse. The legislation is frequently changed to include the new starting products, or potential ones, in order to pre-empt the criminal.

One great mystery in the struggle to control subsidiary chemicals was the continuing supply of solvent necessary for the manufacture of cocaine in Colombia. Informants and aerial surveys confirmed an annual export rate of 1100 tons of the drug from that region. To produce so much cocaine, the manufacturers would need to use 20 000 tons of the solvent, which was a controlled substance and therefore no longer available to the Colombians and others through the traditional channels.

Profiling cocaine and heroin does not tell the investigators where the processing chemicals come from. The DEA had to determine that by making raids on jungle laboratories, studying the barrels to discover the batch coding of the chemicals in use, then relating them to customs import documents.

'All lines in the investigation,' says an agent, 'indicated that the great majority of chemicals being used were imported from western Europe, principally through brokers in Hamburg and Rotterdam.'

This finding reflects on the true nature of the free-for-all trade in chemicals. There is also the problem of eastern Europe generally, where state controls are being removed, so the requirement for greater controls works against the overall economic policies of that area.

There is a considerable degree of hypocrisy, too, where the chemical companies put on the appearance of complying with the restrictive regulations, but carry on dealing with brokers who are not legally required to disclose who their customers are.

As attempts to control the trade in chemicals continue, slowly and painfully, it becomes clearer that the easiest and most accessible approach for controlling the proliferation of drugs is through the individual. In the 1980s, when the Reagan administration realized that a military war on sources of production was having no appreciable effect on the influx of drugs, the government turned its attention to ways of targeting individual users, and deterring those who did not yet use drugs. Nancy Reagan backed the initiative with her 'Say NO' policy, aimed mainly at schoolchildren. As other schemes grew up it was clear that the new legislation would need an effective means, or series of means, to ensure it was adequately enforced. Organized programmes of drug screening would have to be introduced, but in a way that would not disaffect the voters.

The decision to mass-screen people for drugs was not new. It had been done during the Vietnam war, when military personnel returning to civilian life had to submit to a urine drug-analysis as part of the rehabilitation process. In the late 1970s, when an aircraft crashed on to the deck of the carrier *Nimitz*, an investigation revealed that the accident had been drug related. In 1982 the US Navy began routine testing of all personnel for drugs, and it was soon decided that serving personnel in all the services should be screened.

'To initiate the legislation,' says a researcher, 'the scientists had to face the prospect of tests on over a million employees in the military. They had to come up with a test that was rapid and

cheap and could be guaranteed to pick out all the positive cases. The answer was chemical detection.'

The big difference for the chemists setting up the testing of personnel, as distinct from analytical chemists like Ben Perillo, was that personnel tests had to be aimed at detecting parts-per-million of a drug in a person's system. 'They have bags full,' as one chemist put it, 'but we have the equivalent of a tennis ball in the Atlantic Ocean.'

Cost was also crucial, since the test had not only to be carried out on a vast number of people, it had to be done three times a year.

The answer finally chosen was the technique known as immunoassay. In ordinary clinical practice the immunoassay is a test which will measure the protein that takes part in the reaction of an antigen (a substance that triggers the formation of antibodies) with its own specific antibody. The central trick of the technique which makes it useful for detecting drugs is its sensitivity: nothing of a potent nature escapes its attention.

'An immunoassay will detect by-products of cocaine, heroin, cannabis, speed, things like that,' a chemist says, 'but although the test was tuned towards drug detection, it also picked up a number of innocent proteins people had consumed, though not so clearly as the drug traces.'

In other words, the immunoassay would isolate a number of probable drug users, but these people had to be submitted to further testing by the relatively expensive method of mass spectrometry.

'But the point is, with the immunoassay it was possible to narrow down the field dramatically – the expensive testing was only carried out on a small percentage of suspect cases.'

Mass spectrometry is particularly good at drug analysis, so the results of tests, positive or negative, were always dramatically clear.

In 1986 drug testing in the United States moved into civilian life, when Ronald Reagan established compulsory testing of all federal employees and job applicants. This was followed by the 1988 Drug-Free Workplace Act that required all companies obtaining government contracts worth $25 000 or more to promote a drug-free work environment.

Penalties were designed to be adequately deterrent. In the military, those found guilty of using drugs were court-martialled. It was wisely decided not to expel them from the service, since that might easily have resulted in a badly depleted army, navy and air force. In civilian jobs dismissal was the rule; nowadays, those found to be using drugs face dismissal or the option of treatment in a detoxification programme.

The legislation threw open the doors to the widespread implementation of drug screening at all levels and in all sectors of private business. The Office for National Drug Control Policy promotes the idea that it makes good sense: since most people are employed, the workplace may be the most strategic point in society from which to combat the scourge of drugs.

In Britain as in the States, drug testing has reached the employment sector, though not yet in such an all-embracing way; mostly the testing is carried out in jobs where safety is crucial. However, although it is believed that drug testing of employees enhances general safety and leads to a reduction in absenteeism, there are legal possibilities which make the approach to mass screening a matter for some caution.

'Somebody could definitely sue a company for a hefty amount if they wrongly dismissed him on the evidence of a drug test,' says a solicitor. 'The company would have to be dead sure it had a solid system of testing with the lowest margin of error, and decent facilities for double-checking individual samples. Otherwise, with the sheer numbers of people who would be screened every year, any system with flaws in it would soon end up costing employers a lot of money.'

Toxicologist Brian Finkle says that the so-called civilian testing really cloaks a system of cracking down on criminal behaviour. 'On the face of it, it appears there is a separation between the criminal and the civil, but in the way the science is performed, and in its function, there is no distinction between the two. The science is performed in a forensic way, as it should be, because the procedure and the outcome of the test must be legally defensible. That being so, the findings have serious weight, the kind that could lead to imprisonment if the evidence were handled by the State. In the case of a job applicant screened by a prospective employer, the individual could end up being rejected – an effective penalty for taking drugs.

As things stand, the present testing methods are far from ideal. A urine sample is used, and since urine testing only works within four days of taking drugs, an individual can stop taking the drug four days before a test is due to be made. Also, urine testing is intrusive, because the production of a sample has to be supervised to avoid the chance of samples being swapped.

An applicant for a security van driver's job is indignantly eloquent on that point.

'They told me to go into the cubicle and put a sample in the little pot I'd find in there,' he says. 'That was fair enough, I'd made sure I hadn't been for a while so I'd have no trouble giving them what they wanted. But then when I went into the cubicle, this other bloke came in with me. Now it was a one-person cubicle, anybody could see that, so I asked him what he was doing. He said he had to be there to supervise the production of the specimen. Well I told him something flippant, like I knew how to do it without being supervised, something like that, but he went all grim and said it was a ruling, he had to be there.

'Well, all my life I've had this stricture. I can't pass urine if somebody else is around, which is why I made a fuss in the first place. It's not what you'd call a nightmare exactly, but it has made life difficult because I can't often use public facilities, unless I can be sure there's going to be no one else there. I've

always been that way and I told this man that, but he just shrugged as if to say tough, you'll have to learn. So I looked at him and he looked at me and I said he would definitely have to get well outside before I could perform. The he got specific, he said he had to be there so that I didn't swap my urine sample for another one.

'I'd never heard anything so silly. I told him to search me, he said no, he couldn't do that, he had no authority to do such a thing. But you've got authority to look over my shoulder while I'm having a pee, I said. He shrugged again. We had to go back to the interview room and get it sorted out.'

In the end the applicant was allowed to demonstrate that he was carrying no hidden samples of urine, and was then allowed to produce a sample in private.

'But I didn't get the job, even with the brilliant record I've got,' he says, 'and I know it was because I couldn't be relied on to let them have a sample when they felt like asking for one. Afterwards, when I took time to sit and think about it, I was glad I didn't get to work for them. I don't think I like the idea of having a employer sticking his nose that far into my business, whatever his solid gold reasons might be.'

A new technique of drug screening overcomes the difficulties of intrusiveness, and it does not have the time limitations associated with a urine sample. A sample of hair is taken and submitted to chemical testing for hard drugs, which, like a number of poisons, show up in the shaft of the hair.

'It isn't the fastest test, or the simplest, or by any means the cheapest,' says a chemist, 'but it is time-tested for reliability – it's been used for years for poisons testing – and it eliminates, at a stroke, all the difficulty associated with urine testing.'

A Cardiff woman found that the only way she could get her children back from care was to prove she had come off cocaine.

Every month she would visit her doctor, who would snip a hair off the back of her head and submit it for testing. In time, as the cocaine worked its way out of the woman's system, the hair tested negative for the drug. She got back her children.

The test works the other way, too. In Canada a newborn baby was hair-tested for cocaine and the result was positive. Social services took the child away from her mother.

Brian Finkle says there are procedures in forensic chemistry that can test for anything. Emphasis does not have to be placed on how well science can detect drugs, but on the way the results are evaluated before they are accepted. The hair test, as an example, is open to misuse, albeit unwittingly, and the correct procedure before it is implemented would be to submit it to a trial admissibility in a court – in America this is known as a Frye hearing, after a notable case where many of the rules for admissibility were established. The problem with the hair procedure, Finkle believes, is that it is being implemented before it has been adequately assessed. Hair is very absorbent and as yet a threshold level for drug presence has not been established, not have the techniques of testing been standardized.

In the early years of urine testing for drugs, there were a number of setbacks, simply because the technique was implemented before the appropriate checks and balances had been established and implemented.

The navy tests were the battleground. In the early stages of screening, a number of naval officers were court-martialled when their urine samples tested positive for cannabis. Several of them denied they had used drugs and explained away the positive urine test as the result of passive smoking. Because of this legal nicety, thorough studies had to be conducted to determine a threshold level at which positive results were accepted as proof that an individual had been using drugs.

It was also found, on cumulative evidence, that a number of foods could produce effects in urine that swayed drug-test results and could, at certain concentrations, show that drugs were present in the system, when in fact none had been used at all. The urine tests had to be suspended until they were correctly adapted to allow for the new criteria, and then adequately tested.

Brian Finkle says that the evidence of the urine testing programme in the early days shows, clearly, that a new use of science cannot be immediately put into service as a wonder tool – especially not in a programme of mass screening.

Many of the problems with urine testing were ironed out by the military, and a threshold was found which became acceptable in criminal courts, before it was used in the mass screening of civilians. There has been no such assessment with the hair technologies.

The use of the hair test in Britain has so far been restricted to probation and custodial-care cases, where it has been used to show that an individual has stayed off a drug. Its use so far, therefore, has been for negative rather than positive evaluation. It has not yet been used to convict anyone for drug taking, although at the time of writing there are two cases pending, where hair-test evidence for proof of drug taking is to be presented for appraisal in court.

In America, initial reactions to hair testing in several states have been mixed. In some courts the evidence has been admitted on its own, in others a urine test has been demanded in addition to the hair test.

At least in the courts the strengths of the new technology can be tested and its limitations can be uncovered and taken into account. Recently there has been a disturbing trend in the employment market: companies across the United States have begun using hair testing as part of their pre-employment requirements, with no other supporting evidence.

Such a state of affairs is equitable within employment, where there is the right of legal redress, and the technology or the results of a test can be disputed in court. For pre-employment testing no such opportunity open to the individual. As the law stands, prospective employers can perform a urine test and never let the subject know the results, and they can refuse a job without ever providing a reason.

There is a fine irony apparent in recently published figures. The US government, it will be recalled, introduced drug testing with a view to increasing safety at work, reducing absenteeism and sharply reducing the numbers of people using drugs. Last year the American National Academy of Science was given *carte blanche* by the government to assess how well employee testing had fared in its stated goals. After due study, the Academy announced that in matters of safety at work, absenteeism and drug usage among employees, the testing programmes appeared to have had no effect whatsoever.

We have to ask ourselves, says Brian Finkle, why forensic testing in civil matters is making such huge and rapid inroads into Western societies while it is still such an unknown quantity and before its consequences have been properly considered.

In America, at least, the commercial implications are perfectly clear. Employment testing has become a multi-million-dollar business. The company which carries out large-scale hair testing has just been the subject of a partial takeover by a bigger company. There is a powerful lobby in Congress to see these technologies pushed through the legislature and made law. The source of the pressure, however, is commercial rather than legal. In the long term, the ultimate validity of hair testing will be argued in the courts, but that will not be until many people have been wrongly dismissed on drug-related charges, and many have been unfairly disqualified from taking jobs.

It is clear that chemical detection plays a very important role in the war against drugs but, as Brian Finkle has remarked, it can never be a chemical fix. It is a tool which can have huge and unpleasant repercussions if it is used without proper care and without proper consideration of the circumstances where it might be deemed appropriate.

Where forensic science has become separated from the crime-detection environment where its *raison d'être* is constantly challenged and assessed, it can become a tool propelled solely by commercial imperatives.

the
ver

dict

Scientists are fallible and have been known to make serious mistakes. Their work is not always conducted along objective lines, nor do they always do it in an impartial frame of mind. Two straightforward statements, not notably controversial, yet they go against a vast body of instinctive belief and ingrained expectation. To many people the essence of the scientist, indeed of science, is a quality close to immaculacy.

The one class of witness juries tend to trust implicitly is the scientific specialist, the expert witness who gets into the box and speaks his spotless truth. Freud recognized this inclination to special trust among the public, the tendency to glorify scientists and their works, and he made a point of telling people that it was wrong to believe science consists of nothing but conclusively proved propositions, and it was *very* wrong to expect as much.

'It is a demand only made by those who feel a craving for authority in some form,' he wrote, *'and a need to replace the religious catechism by something else, even if it be a scientific one.'*

The reputed reliability of forensic science, long taken for granted, has always been able to stand up to tremors as long as they did not affect the foundations. Forensic science suffered no serious loss of grace when, for instance, it was revealed that Ralph E. Erdmann, MD, a Medical Examiner in Lubbock County, Texas, had been reporting the findings of autopsies he had never performed. The misdemeanour was discovered when a body was exhumed for a second opinion on the cause of death, as certified by Dr Erdmann, and it was found there had never been an autopsy in the first place.

In due course Erdmann found himself being indicted by a grand jury for 'knowingly and intentionally' falsifying an autopsy report and for having billed the county $650 for a service he never undertook. The case was not unique and its implications, although serious, were not thought to have lasting or wide-ranging effects. In the public eye, Dr Erdmann's case was no more than an example of a bad apple turning up, as regrettably it will, in a barrel of otherwise flawless fruit.

Bigger cases, however, have produced greater uneasiness. The expertise of scientists and technicians has lately come under fire because of large-scale publicity generated by prosecutions where forensic evidence has been variously flawed, seriously questionable or downright wrong.

Among other cases, that of the so-called Birmingham Six did considerable damage to the reputation of forensic science in the United Kingdom. When 22 people died in the bombing of two Birmingham pubs in November 1974, the police moved quickly, acting on current intelligence, and they picked up their suspects within a few hours. In due course six Irishmen – Richard McIlkenny, John Walker, Hugh Callaghan, Patrick Hill, Gerry Hunter and Billy Power – were convicted of the bombings and were imprisoned. At the trial, confessions by four of the six men were supported by chemical tests which showed that Hill and Power had recently handled explosives. The six men's third appeal against their conviction (the first two were dismissed) hinged on independent forensic evidence which showed that traces of soap or cigarette smoke could have produced the same positive test results. This testimony, together with the revelation that exonerating evidence had been withheld at the original trial, resulted in the Birmingham Six being declared innocent and released on 14 March 1991, after serving 17 years in prison.

By now a substantial worldwide body of criticism has grown up against forensic science. Some of it has surfaced only after years of festering unreported, because in many cases the criticisms were simply not taken seriously. The range of censure is wide and some of it can be summarized here.

Cost

Since forensic scientific procedures are expensive, they can be used at their fullest capability only in a small number of cases. The cost also means that the police have to exercise careful judgement in their use of professional forensic services, and that, in turn, means they will sometimes be over-cautious, forgoing expert opinion that might well influence the outcome of certain cases.

SOCOs

In Great Britain the police train their own Scene of Crime Officers (SOCOs), which means that police employees carry out the forensic examination of a crime scene; they also make the reconstruction of the crime. SOCOs and their direct superiors determine the probable train of events leading to a crime; they decide how the evidence will be approached, and what evidence will be the subject of the eventual forensic evaluation of the scene of crime. Such an arrangement leaves very little room for objectivity.

Time

Forensic laboratories usually take a long time to process their workload. Frequent long delays in the production of vital evidence create a bottleneck in the judicial system and often hamper detective work.

Negligence

Since the Birmingham Six case, and others, the reliability of science in the service of justice has been keenly questioned. Even when tests can be shown to be reliable, no such guarantee can ever be made for the people conducting the tests. More cross-checking has been recommended, but there is no evidence that it has been implemented to any significant extent – nor is it a likely development in an atmosphere of perpetual cost cutting.

Prosecution bias

Forensic science establishments have traditionally been connected to police departments, and that is certainly still true in the United States. Forensic science services in the UK are under the control of the Home Office, but there is still the possibility of forensic scientists and the police, both being servants of the government, taking a joint view of a case which leaves no room for healthy scepticism on the part of the scientist. The interpretation of results may also be affected by a similarity of outlook on the part of policeman and scientist. This last appears to be more of a problem in the USA than in Britain.

Expert witnesses

The expert witness industry in the United States is very big business. Some professionals spend their entire working lives going from court to court, rendering their opinions for often large fees. They invariably testify in terms of 'certainty', scarcely ever referring to the countless uncertainties of science. There are places like the Medical Consulting Service of Rockville, Maryland, which advertises, 'If the first doctor we refer doesn't agree with your legal theory, we will provide you with the name of a second.'

Expert witness bias

The conscious or unconscious bias of scientists is a troubling point arising from the one above. When a scientist is employed by one of two sides, can he or she ever be neutral?

Passive defence

Expert witnesses appearing for the prosecution rarely have their testimony challenged with any force, or at noticeable length. One way to ensure a sound presentation of a forensic case is to have a good hard cross-examination of prosecution forensic witnesses, instead of the more usual complaisance on the part of the defence. Better still would be a competent defence forensic scientist, but the limitations of legal aid in the UK make this an unlikely scenario.

An attorney with the US Department of Justice has suggested that criminal prosecution should be used more actively to deter and condemn some forms of scientific misconduct. While the attorney did not specifically name forensic scientists as the culprits, they are obviously involved. Some of the types of misconduct targeted are:

1 reporting tests that were never made
2 misrepresentation of test or research results
3 'cooking' information – e.g. reporting only data which support a particular conclusion
4 trimming results, so that data which are in conflict with the scientist's belief are lopped off in the reporting
5 the failure to establish or follow a set protocol for conducting tests
6 a failure to record data, which may be a cover for not having run particular tests
7 acquiring financial or other interest in the testing, thereby creating a conflict in the scientist's ability to be objective.

In Britain there have been calls for a swifter acceptance of change among forensic scientists. One British forensic pathologist has talked about the way ancient and often discredited tests and fallacious causes of death have been cherished too long by men and women who simply do not want to be troubled by progress.

'Take status lymphaticus as an example,' the pathologist says. 'It's actually a hypothetical thing, sometimes called status thymo-lymphaticus, and nowadays it's generally held to be *indefensible as a cause of death. It was very much in vogue in the first half of this century as an explanation of certain sudden deaths where no real cause could be found.'*

The thymus gland in the chest normally shrinks at puberty, but in some individuals it continues to grow; its presence sometimes accompanies other unusual internal features such as larger-than-usual lymph glands, and sometimes underdevelopment of large blood vessels, such as the aorta.

'It used to be believed that people, young people, especially young adults with this condition, were especially prone to sudden death from very trivial causes,' the pathologist says, *'sometimes no more than a bump being enough to despatch them. The thing was, these deaths left no sign that could be seen at autopsy, and the condition was often mixed up with vagal inhibition, another rather shaky cause of death.'*

Following a lot of debate in the medical press, much of it between the two world wars, the condition of *status lymphaticus* was less and less put forward as a cause, or a contributing cause, in cases of unexplained sudden death in young people. It is still thought possible that some people with persistent thymus glands and underdeveloped aortas are prone to sudden death from reasonably trivial causes, but proving the link in many cases would be impossible. *Status lymphaticus* was not scientifically formulated as a medical condition, and, worse, it was a negative finding: when it was entered as a cause of death there was no need to show its presence, since an absence of signs was taken by many doctors to be a prime indication that *status lymphaticus* was the culprit.

'Most forensic pathologists would agree it's probably non-existent. It was a convenient invention, nothing more. But even so, as recently as the early to mid 1960s, status lymphaticus was still being inserted as the cause of death in certificates written by certain practitioners who simply would not depart from the old ways. They were the kind who still exist, in later versions, who

*believe a doctor should show some consistency in his approach
to his craft, and the way to do that is to refuse to absorb
anything new, and to avoid change at all costs.'*

More than a few such people, says the pathologist, are involved
in forensic work in the UK.

*'They hang on to all the knowledge they picked up God-knows-
how-many years ago, and they turn a blind eye to any
newfangled stuff that came along after that. It's sickening
behaviour in people who are supposed to embody the scientific
approach in their work, but as long as traditionalism remains a
virtue, they'll be around.'*

Another and perhaps more damning example of forensic
specialists refusing to move with the times is shown by the way
some pathologists test the lungs of dead babies to decide whether
they were born alive.

*'For a lot of years,' says the pathologist, 'the "hydrostatic test"
was used to determine whether lungs had or hadn't breathed.
Pieces of lung were dropped in water to see if they would float
or sink. If they floated it meant the child had once been alive
outside of the mother. If they sank, the child had never legally
been alive. It was utter nonsense.'*

Some doctors still have faith in the hydrostatic test, and they
still apply its methods for obtaining proof of live birth. In spite of the
fact that it was pointed out, long ago, that even a tiny degree of
decomposition will make lungs and lung fragments float, the
diehards responded by introducing a procedure of sandwiching the
lung between sheets of newspaper and stepping on it, thereby
expelling 'additional gas', in other words the gas produced by
putrefactive change. It was argued, and by some is still argued, that
the microscopic globules of air trapped in the fine tissue of a baby's
lung cannot be expelled by stepping on it, or by any other simple
means, and it will therefore remain as a sound indication that the

lung once drew breath into a living child.

Enlightened pathologists agree that the most apt description of the hydrostatic test is in Polson and Gee's *Essentials of Forensic Medicine*, published in 1973, which says:

The test was suspect in 1900 and requires no detailed discussion, because it is now known to have no value.

'Try telling that to some of the fogeys who swear by it,' says the pathologist. 'You can point out, at the top of your voice and until you're blue in the neck, that the hydrostatic test for viability is entirely without scientific foundation, and all you'll make them do is cling harder to the procedure.' He shakes his head. 'Floating and sinking lungs. It's bizarre. If you ask me, it's no different from a belief in witchcraft.'

The whole area of proving and disproving live birth is of crucial importance in forensic work, since evidence of separate existence is the means by which a charge of murder or infanticide can be brought. Separate existence is not the same thing as live birth: a child may show signs of life when it is halfway out of the mother, but those signs may disappear before the child's feet leave the birth canal. Separate existence, in law, requires that the whole infant be expelled from the body (but this requirement does not include the umbilical cord or the placenta). If the child loses all signs of life before it leaves the mother's body, then it has had no separate existence.

'Something so fundamental to the human condition is bound to attract the witch doctors,' the pathologist says. 'Some of them believe they're being very scientific when they say they measure the cells lining the air passages – they take that as an index of breathing, even when it's been shown that changes in those cells are related to maturity in the child, not breathing.'

Naked-eye evaluation of fresh lungs at autopsy, carried out by an experienced pathologist, is the only reliable test for viability of an infant. Where there is relative pinkness, sponginess and a certain crackling to the touch, then most probably the infant had a separate existence. When the signs are less than these, no decision can be taken and benefit of the doubt is given to whoever may have been suspected of child destruction.

'It isn't a method that requires hocus pocus, and it doesn't need complex and flashy examination equipment, either,' says the pathologist. 'It's reliable, though. It has evolved and has been adopted by those who want to keep abreast of developments. The others, the ones immune to progress, will stick to their prejudices, no matter how much harm they do.'

A lax approach and rigid adherence to half-understood principles would not seem to be ideal credentials for a man whose job was to establish causes of death, yet one such man was, until his sudden death in 1989, a much admired police surgeon in an area south of London. Colleagues doing forensic work for neighbouring police administrations knew of the doctor's shortcomings, but at least one has admitted that loyalty, most of it induced by the man's 'likeable' nature, kept them silent throughout his long and superficially bright career. One person, however, did complain, and for his pains he was told in various semi-official ways to mind his own business.

'I'm a paramedic, a competent one I think, and my work often took me across the path of this person we'll call Dr George. Some of the blunders I witnessed nearly made me scream. The thing was, though, he was good in a law court, he was a really good talker so he made an effective witness – a lot like Spilsbury [the British pathologist who made his name at the Crippen trial], I suppose, and he was another one who wasn't half as good as his line of patter suggested he was.'

The paramedic first met Dr George when they attended the scene of a sudden death. The deceased was a young woman in her early twenties. She was curled up on her side on the bed, fully clothed. Beside her, on the bedside table, was a box which contained a vaginal douche syringe.

'Dr George began putting two and two together,' the paramedic says. 'He decided it was a classic case of delayed embolism. She had used the syringe with hot water to try and abort herself, had straightened her clothing again and tidied away afterwards. Then she had felt funny and had lain down on the bed. That was when the embolism hit her heart, according to Dr George. Absolutely classic case, he said. She had died in just the position we found her.'

Dr George had voiced his hypothesis to a roomful of medical auxiliaries and a couple of police officers. They had all listened respectfully. Then a murder team arrived and asked everyone to leave the room. Dr George assumed that did not include him. He stayed, and from the hallway the paramedic heard him repeat his theory to the forensic pathologist and the SOCOs.

'It went a bit quiet after that,' the paramedic recalls, 'then Dr George came out, nodded kind of sheepishly to myself and the ambulance driver, and he left. Five minutes later they asked us if we could now help move the body. When we went in the pathologist was tagging a bottle of tablets. Barbiturates, he told us. He said the girl had taken so many her mouth was full of half-dissolved capsules.'

On another occasion Dr George reported that in his view, a deceased person had been dead for no longer than ten hours. The timing was very important, because it could place certain individuals near the scene of the death – which was a murder – while others could not have been there at all.

'I saw that body at the same time as Dr George did,' says the paramedic. 'It was lying naked in a bedroom with what would have been an average spring temperature. There was a greenish tinge over the dead man's right iliac fossa, I could smell acetone, and rigor mortis was wearing off. Everything told me the

deceased had been dead for about two days, possibly longer. But Dr George would have none of that. He even told me, with his patronizing smile that some people took for charm, that he was the one trained in forensic work, and besides, he had an instinct for times of death.'

On another occasion, Dr George visited a house where a man and his daughter had both been found dead. The man, a chronic invalid, was in bed, the daughter was in a chair beside the bed. There was a strong smell of gas (it was in the days of poisonous coal gas) and one look at the dead woman told Dr George she had died of carbon monoxide poisoning,

'Classic signs, he told everybody,' the paramedic recalls. 'The redness in the features, pink fingernails, bright cherry-red appearance in the blood sample that was drawn off from the woman's arm. But even the constable who had been first into the house had noticed that the dead man had none of those signs. He was blue around the mouth and at the extremities, he was stiff while his daughter wasn't – yet Dr George was quite happy to issue death certificates on both of them, certifying the cause of death in both instances as carbon monoxide poisoning. He ventured the mature opinion, strictly on the side, that it was a suicide pact.'

What had probably happened, the paramedic believes, was that the daughter, a woman in her late forties who had cared for her father for 20 years, had found him dead in bed – highly probable in view of the fact he had a chronic and worsening heart condition. Time had passed and she had decided that her life was empty without her father, so she turned on the gas and sat by his bed to wait for the fumes to overcome her. It was not a new scenario in the paramedic's experience; the only new feature was the spectacle of an accredited police surgeon unable to see that two people had died from quite obviously different causes.

The third case of Dr George, another one the paramedic said he will never forget, concerned a child who was taken to a mortuary as a suspected cot death. She was two years old, well-nourished and clean. The paramedic was one of the team who had tried to revive the child. When they had failed, the paramedic brought the body to the mortuary. Dr George was there, filling out cremation papers. He looked at the child's body and told the paramedic she had passed away exactly as the parents claimed – she had simply died of SIDS – Sudden Infant Death Syndrome.

'When I looked at the body in the strong mortuary light I had other ideas,' the paramedic said. 'For a start, she had bruises on her arms and there was a nasty lump on the back of her head. Then I felt the abdomen – it was distended and boggy. I went back to the office and mentioned that to Dr George. He said he'd noticed the abdomen, too, but in his view the swelling and the pulpy feel were caused by the early stages of decomposition. This, remember, in a child who had been dead only a few hours.'

The family doctor refused to issue a death certificate. A post mortem examination of the child showed that she had been beaten to death. Her abdomen was filled with blood from a ruptured liver.

'Dr George actually had the nerve to tell me, without blinking, that he thought the pathologist had made a mistake about the abdomen,' the paramedic says. 'There were times, I swear, when I could believe he had no medical training at all. Yet there he was, working away as part of the forensic establishment. I wouldn't say he was typical, but the system accommodated him, didn't it? It makes you wonder.'

At present there is a tendency for the public to believe that the major 'problematic' area of forensic science is DNA profiling, and in both America and Great Britain it has come under increasing attack, notably in the press. However, according to Michael Saks, a Professor of Law at the University of Iowa, and a number of other academics and scientists, DNA profiling is already – and increasingly will be – the least troublesome and indeed the most respectable area of forensic science.

At this point, two definitions may be in order:

DNA is deoxyribonucleic acid, a self-replicating material found in nearly all living organisms, which is the carrier of genetic information, the so-called 'genetic blueprint' giving each individual his or her unique characteristics.

DNA profiling is any one of several techniques for analysing and comparing DNA from different sources (see pages 59-60). According to Professor Saks, it stands head and shoulders above most other forensic techniques because, before it was adopted into the forensic arena, it grew out of rigorous development programmes within twentieth-century academic and industrial laboratories. Meticulous standards of procedure and exhaustive cross-checking were applied to DNA testing at all its stages of development, ensuring that it now stands as an investigative technique firmly rooted in good science.

'The debate over DNA fingerprinting,' Saks wrote in the Cardozo Law Review, 'may compel the rest of forensic science to become more recognizably scientific.'

Relatively little scientific scrutiny, he argues, has been applied to the areas of identification by hair, fibres, tool-marks, bite-marks and, to a lesser extent, fingerprints. In the past century, he goes on, identification science has been very successful in the courts of law, but the success has been accomplished by the use of many tactics which good science rejects, such as the concealment of assumptions, reliance on intuition rather than the collection and computation of data, shunning an experimental approach in preference to relying on established theory, and failing to submit its own cherished theories to objective scientific testing.

Perhaps, Saks concludes, because criminal trials call for strong identification evidence, and because judges are badly equipped to evaluate so-called science, forensic science has virtually walked through an open door into the courtroom without ever being properly scrutinized.

The situation may be set to change. Demands for greater controls and more empirical testing of established procedures are coming from people who are not easy to ignore. The story of Dr Michael West, which follows, illustrates some of the slackness and uncertainties that have alerted a growing body of observers to call for radical reforms in the structure and the practice of forensic science.

On Friday, 7 September 1990, during the lunchtime break of a group of pulpwood cutters on Triple Pipeline Road in Lauderdale County, near Daleville, Mississippi, the men heard what they took to be gunshots. The time was approximately 12.30 p.m. Two and a half hours later, a number of police units responded to a call made to central despatch, and went to a house close to the spot where the cutters were working. The first units arrived at 3.17 p.m. According to records filed at the Circuit Court of Kemper County, the police found a scene out of a horror movie.

There were three bodies. One was identified as Mamie Parker, the 68-year-old wife of Floyd 'Dan' Parker; 91-year-old Floyd lay nearby; and near him was the body of 75-year-old Susie Harvey, sister of Mamie Parker.

Autopsies determined that Susie Harvey had died of a fractured skull (blunt trauma) and had multiple cuts and stab wounds; Mamie Parker had been shot by a small-bore firearm, but was killed by stabbing and cutting; Floyd Parker also died of stabbing and cutting.

The old people had been seen by a neighbour at noon on the day they died, and she testified that they were fine at that time. Deputies discovered that a man called Larry Maxwell, great-nephew of Floyd Parker, had been a regular visitor to the Parker house and had possibly borrowed money from them.

A search warrant was obtained for the home of Mrs Catherine

McWilliams, with whom Larry Maxwell lived, just half a mile from the scene of the crime. A .22 calibre pistol and a butcher's knife with a broken handle were found at the house.

Forensic testing detected no blood on the knife, but the gun was positively identified as the weapon which had fired the bullets taken from the body of Mamie Parker.

When Larry Maxwell was brought in to the police station several days later, Chief Deputy Michael Vick wanted to have his hands examined for trace metal, to see if he had handled the gun. Dr Michael West was called in. West was a forensic odontologist (bite-mark examiner) and a reputed expert in the use of a technique called alternative light imaging, which he used to detect wound patterns. He had already examined the three murder victims but, he said in this instance, examining the hands of Larry Parker was probably just a waste of time, because it had been seven days since the murders and trace metal doesn't stay around as long as that.

However, to satisfy Deputy Vick, West examined Larry Maxwell's hands in the illumination from his 'blue light', and claimed to find positive evidence that Maxwell had handled the butcher's knife. He later wrote separate letters – on 13 and 17 September – addressed to Chief Deputy Vick, confirming his findings. In the first letter he wrote:

> *On 11 Sep 90, at the request of Dr Steve Hayne, I did travel to Pearl Ms to examine the bodies of Floyd Parker approx 91 y/o black male, Susie Harvey approx 75 y/o black female and Mamie Parker approx 68 y/o black female. I was given a butcher knife by Chief Dep. Michael Vick to compare to the wounds. He also supplied me with a portion of a door with a slash mark for comparison.*

Findings
> *Two marks were compared on the body of Floyd Parker: on the neck at the base of the right ear, over the left*

collar bone. Two marks on the body of Mamie Parker: front of left shoulder, left upper lip. Two marks on the body of Susie Harvey: right collar bone, central area of back.

Opinion

The wounds on the body of Floyd Parker were indeed and without doubt produced by the butcher knife in question.

The wounds on the body of Mamie Parker were indeed and without doubt produced by the butcher knife in question.

The slash mark on the door was indeed and without doubt produced by the butcher knife in question.

The wounds on the body of Susie Harvey are consistent with the butcher knife in question.

In the second letter he wrote:

On 14 Sep 90, I did travel to the Lauderdale County S.O. At approximately 7.00 p.m. I was given a court order to examine one Larry Maxwell. I was assisted by Michael Cole. Mr Maxwell's hands were examined, photographed and compared to a butcher knife, which I had examined earlier.

Opinion

The knife in question did indeed and without doubt make the patterns made on the hands of one Larry Maxwell. The patterns on his hands were produced by holding the knife and striking an object or objects several times with each hand. The blows would have been of great intensity.

At the subsequent trial of Larry Maxwell, Dr West testified for the prosecution. The defence responded with the accusation that West had used a scientifically unacceptable technique to link

Maxwell to the knife used in the three murders. Forensic experts taking the stand in support of the defence allegations said that West's evidence was worthless.

'I cannot accept this as scientific evidence,' said Dr Robert Kirchner, a forensic pathologist and Deputy Medical Examiner in Chicago. He pointed to the fact that West had claimed to find marks on Maxwell's hands that showed he handled the fatal knife, but he failed to capture the marks on photographs; there was no evidence they ever existed. 'Dr West looks at Mr Maxwell's hands, claims he sees something, can't photograph it, so he free-hands a sketch of it. I have no way of judging what he saw or didn't see,' Kirchner told the court. 'It's nonsense, not science.'

A move was made by the defence attorneys to have Dr West charged with perjury. The judge duly considered the motion, and in his carefully weighed conclusion he said, among other things, that Dr West's scientific impartiality did appear to be in question. He cited the following exchange:

Question:
Now, that day of September 14th, 1990, when you saw what were apparently patterns on Mr Maxwell's hands, did you believe that you had stumbled across an exciting new area?

Answer:
I thought it was the best thing since sliced bread. This is not a pattern that someone left. It's not a pattern that the attacker left on the victim. This is a pattern that the attacker leaves in the palm of his hand. The old phrase, you caught them red-handed – to me, caught them blue-handed. I put a blue light on it and, boom, there's the pattern of the weapon. I was ecstatic.

In short, the judge said, Dr West had the knife that law

enforcement officials had identified to him as the suspected murder weapon. He had before him the accused man, the man that the law enforcement officers had identified as the perpetrator of a multiple murder. The process in and of itself was suggestive. It was thoroughly unobjective.

Moreover, Dr West could not replicate or duplicate what he saw with his naked eyes when he examined Larry Maxwell's hands. It appeared clear to the judge that Dr West had not carried out analysis, supporting photography or any of the other work that would have lent strength and credibility to his opinion.

On the matter of admissibility, the judge quoted from the opinion rendered in the key case of Frye versus the United States. In that case the DC Circuit Court of Appeals stated:

Just when a scientific principle or discovery crosses the line between the experimental and demonstrable stages is difficult to define. Somewhere in the twilight zone the evidential force of the principle must be recognized, and while courts will go a long way in admitting expert testimony deduced from a well-recognized scientific principle or discovery, the thing from which the deduction is made must be sufficiently established to have gained general acceptance in the particular field in which it belongs.

On the basis of that statement the judge said, 'It is my considered opinion that the State has failed to show that Dr West's novel technique of forensic alternative light imaging for the purpose of detecting trace wound patterns on human skin is a technique and practice that's generally accepted within the forensic science field.'

In another case, the judge said, that of the People versus Castro, the New York court stated that novel scientific evidence must pass a three-prong test: the theory must be generally accepted, the techniques must be generally accepted, and the general techniques must have been performed properly. In the case before the court, the judge continued, the techniques used by Dr West on Larry Marshall were of little value, scientifically unproven, and not yet validated or accepted by most of his peers.

'It may well be that Dr West is a pioneer in the field of alternative light imaging for the purpose of detecting trace wound patterns on the human skin,' the report went on, 'and it may well be that the future will prove that his techniques are sound evidentiary tools that result in the presentation of inherently reliable expert opinions. But at this time, I am not so convinced.'

Finally, the judge said, the court was not convinced that probable cause existed to believe that Dr Michael West wilfully and intentionally committed an act of perjury when he testified before the court in the Larry Maxwell case. So the motion to hold him in contempt and to incarcerate him was denied. But so was his testimony.

Eventually Larry Maxwell was set free. Under the heading 'LITTLE CHANCE OF SOLVING SLAYINGS', a front-page column on the *Mississippi Meridian Star* told the story.

With the District Attorney's prime suspect gone, authorities say there's little hope the community will ever know who killed three elderly Daleville residents.

'We certainly have no new leads in the case,' said Joe Sciple, Sheriff of Kemper County, who assisted Lauderdale County law enforcement officers in the initial investigation. 'We were satisfied with the one who was accused of doing it,' he said on Thursday, after Lauderdale County District Attorney Bilbo Mitchell's office dismissed capital murder charges against Larry Maxwell.

Charges were dropped when the State lost its key witness after a ruling by the court that said Dr Michael

> *West's testimony was based on forensic data not commonly accepted by the scientific community.*

One organ of the scientific community was soon having its own say. The journal *Scientific Sleuthing* ran a page on 'The West Phenomenon' with the subheading:

DON'T GO WEST, YOUNG MAN, MISSISSIPPI COURT SAYS; THE 'WEST PHENOMENON' SEEN AS LESS BLUE LIGHT THAN BLUE SMOKE AND MIRRORS

The article was openly sceptical, even mocking, with several references to Dr West's use of the phrase 'indeed and without doubt', and a lengthy demonstration that in the view of forensic scientists in general, the 'blue light' technique was not well understood and was not, in spite of a few supporters, taken very seriously. One short paragraph summed up the tone of the entire piece:

> *As to the use of ultraviolet imaging on Larry Maxwell's hands the court was almost as emphatic in its opinion as Dr West himself was in his 'indeed and without a doubt' opinions. Dr West's techniques were 'of little value, scientifically unproven and not yet validated or accepted by most of his peers', according to the evidence which the court accepted.*

Rumblings grew and spread within scientific and legal circles, and eventually an attorney placed a complaint with the Ethics Committee of the American Academy of Forensic Sciences (AAFS), saying that a Fellow of the AAFS had issued a report in a capital murder case which had been based on procedure not generally recognized in the field. The Ethics Committee considered the complaint and decided there were grounds to believe it could be well founded. An investigation was set in motion.

In the meantime Dr West was involved professionally in a case against Anthony Keko, 63, an oyster fisherman from a district just south of New Orleans. Fourteen months earlier Keko's ex-wife Louise had been found murdered; the police did not at first connect Keko with the murder scene, and indeed he had a strong alibi. A year later, however, the police reopened the case, and this time they had 13 suspects, one of them Anthony Keko. At that point Dr West was engaged to help with the case.

The 14-month-old corpse of the ex-wife was exhumed, and Dr West went to work with his blue light examination technique. Shining the lamp on the body and studying the skin through yellow goggles, he said he could see bruises, which he believed were bite-marks. The marks were then compared with a mould of Anthony Keko's teeth – though not with moulds from the teeth of any other suspects. West said there was a match between the mould and the bruises. He repeated the assertion under oath in court. The jury recommended life imprisonment for Anthony Keko.

The Ethics Committee of the AAFS was meanwhile considering the evidence against Dr West. There were transcripts of court testimony, affidavits in support and in opposition to the respondent, videotape and audiotape of demonstrations by the respondent and copies of numerous papers and articles.

The most potentially damaging accusations included a report that in one capital murder case Dr West had claimed that the fingernails of a deceased individual had 'indeed and without doubt' made scratch marks on a defendant. At any time, even when the investigation is being conducted by an expert on wounds and wounding, it is very difficult to say, with any certainty, that anyone's fingernails caused a particular wound or set of wounds.

The evidence given in the Maxwell case was also being used against West, as was his claim that several other people had used his blue light technique in their work. This last was especially damaging, since three of the people he named had already denied ever doing such work.

In the end, it was the unanimous opinion of the Committee that Dr West had behaved most unprofessionally. They made it clear that his action in identifying certain implements (fingernails included) as having made specific marks, without having made test marks with the implements, and without evaluating the class and individual characteristics, or establishing the reproducibility of marks made by the implements, did not meet the appropriate professional standards.

Overall, the Ethics Committee found that the pattern of activities and disregard for – or non-acceptance of – generally accepted professional standards was such that, in their opinion, Dr West had violated Article II of Section 1a of the by-laws of the Academy:

Every member of the American Academy of Forensic Sciences shall refrain from exercising professional or personal conduct adverse to the best interests and purposes of the Academy.

It was also the opinion of the Committee that Dr West was in conflict with Article II Section 1c:

Every member of the AAFS shall refrain from providing any material misrepresentation of data upon which an expert opinion or conclusion is based.

It was therefore the recommendation of the Ethics Committee to the Board of Directors that Dr Michael H. West, a Fellow of the Odontology Section, be expelled from the Academy for violation of the by-laws.

In the wake of the complaint to the AAFS came another, this time in the form of a request to the Ethics Committee of the American Board of Forensic Odontology (ABFO), asking them to review and rule upon potential ethical violations by Dr West, relating to his testimony and evaluation of evidence in the case of the State versus Larry Maxwell, of Kemper County, Mississippi.

In addition to other evidence, the Ethics Committee was provided with complete court transcripts of the State versus Larry Maxwell. The records were provided both by Dr West in his defence and by attorney John Holdridge in support of the complaint.

After review and consideration of all facts and evidence from both parties, the Ethics Committee of the ABFO arrived at a unanimous conclusion. The summing-up, in part, was as follows:

Dr West, in the opinion of the Committee, did not act in an impartial manner in his testimony regarding the Maxwell evidence. In court testimony Dr West presented the 'West phenomenon' without it being founded on scientific principles. Dr West clearly identified himself as an expert in the field of forensic odontology, yet presented testimony regarding physical evidence that is outside the field of forensic odontology.

The Ethics Committee found and affirmed that the ABFO Code of Ethics and Guiding Principles had been violated by Dr West. They recommended that he receive a one-year suspension of his status as a Diplomat of the American Board of Forensic Odontology.

Shortly afterwards, Anthony Keko petitioned for a new trial. The petition was based on the ground of newly discovered evidence and the failure of the State to disclose exculpatory evidence. The entire motion rested on the fact that Dr West was now a discredited witness, and the following points, among others, were presented in the petition.

- According to police officers during the pre-trial hearings, Mr Keko was only one of many suspects in the police investigation of the unlawful killing of his ex-wife, Zelma Louise Keko; no arrests had or could have been made, and an indictment could not have been returned against Mr Keko. The indictment against Mr Keko was returned only after Dr West made his examination of the corpse and made his opinion about the presence of bruises, and their probable cause, known to the grand jury.

- At the very time he testified at the grand jury, and during the pre-trial proceedings, and at trial, ethical and disciplinary proceedings had been filed against Dr West by both the American Academy of Forensic Sciences and the American Board of Forensic Odontology, and proceedings were pending against him. Dr West was even called upon to (and did) respond to the American Academy of Forensic Sciences charges during the Keko trial.

- At all times Dr West knew of the charges and the pending proceedings. At no time did Dr West or the State ever disclose to the defence that any such proceedings were pending.

- Due to the confidentiality of the proceedings and the State's and Dr West's failure to disclose the proceedings, the defence did not know and could not have known of the existence of the proceedings.

- The pending proceedings of the American Academy of Forensic Sciences and of the American Board of Forensic Odontology constituted exculpatory evidence that was necessary to the defence of Mr Keko, yet the information was not given to the defence.

- After the proceedings and hearing for both groups were concluded, and after Dr West's response to the charges had been considered, both groups concluded that the complaints were well founded and that Dr West must be expelled from the bodies which brought the proceedings against him.

In December 1995, the judge ruled in favour of a retrial for Anthony Keko, pending the results or Dr West's appeal.

In the meantime, in spite of losing his accreditation, Dr West continued to make himself and his forensic services available to any authorities who wished to employ him. Asked to comment on his expulsion from the AAFS and the ABFO, West told the *Meridian Star* that in his opinion the charges against him had been triggered by professional jealousy.

'I told them to forget it, I quit,' he said. 'I gave them my membership certification. I gave them my distinguished membership certification. I don't need those people.'

Since the ruling in the Maxwell case and the surrender of his credentials, West had continued to use his blue-light technique to testify in cases where his evidence had helped to produce convictions. The *Meridian Star* reported that since his expulsion from the AAFS and his suspension from the ABFO, he had testified as a forensic expert in Louisiana in a capital murder case, in two murder cases in Michigan and another in New York State. It was perfectly legal for West to go on practising as a forensic expert, the only difference being that he could not say he was certified by the bodies that expelled him. Being disbarred did not appear to have lightened his case load. 'I've got cases pending in Alabama, Mississippi and Louisiana,' he told a reporter, and he was among a group of experts who could be called in on investigations locally. On top of all that, Dr West still maintained a successful and highly lucrative general dental practice in Mississippi.

To informed observers, the case of Dr Michael West raises again the subject of inexact science being passed off as reliable testimony. So much of West's forensic work was simply subjective, consisting of a series of opinions that gained weight because of a reputation for reliability West had built up over the years, without ever submitting his techniques or his general competence to objective examination.

Misgivings over the blue light technique are easy to understand, once it is realized that the method has no accepted scientific basis, nor can its so-called results usually be demonstrated. But it is just as easy to imagine a jury, ready to accept any assertion made in the name of science, believing that ultraviolet light and coloured goggles could, in the right hands, be the means of performing exceptional feats of detection. It is not surprising that some authorities believe forensic science has enjoyed a reputation and a measure of public trust which, as yet, it does not deserve.

In the Keko case, Dr West said unequivocally that Mr Keko inflicted the bite-marks allegedly present on his ex-wife's dead body. West arrived at his conclusion by the use of highly unscientific methods. The question arises: would the conclusion have been any more reliable if it had been conducted on lines considered more orthodox for the practice of forensic odontology?

Some people hold the view that forensic odontology is more of an art than a science. To gain a little understanding of the work involved, it is worth examining the general subject of bite-marks, and some of the procedures used to record and investigate them. These tasks are often performed by police technicians or by pathologists at the scene of a crime. The following descriptions should give some idea of the room that exists for error, even before a forensic odontologist begins to evaluate a case.

First, another brief definition: **forensic odontology** is concerned with the identification of persons, or their remains, by examination of their teeth. That can mean, by extension, the identification of people by the marks their teeth leave on inanimate objects, or on other people.

Bite-marks on the human body are common, and they are especially common in cases of child abuse and in adult sexual attacks. In sexual cases the bites may be very minor, amounting to no more than light bruising where sucked skin has been drawn into contact with the teeth. In other cases the bites are deep and often penetrating; occasionally a bite will completely remove a chunk of skin and underlying tissue, leaving a crater with edges matching the dental configuration of the biter. Common sites for bites in sexual assaults are the side of the neck and the breasts. Nipples are sometimes bitten off. Biting in sexual attacks is also inflicted on the thighs, abdomen, buttocks and vulva.

Bites are common in the battered child syndrome, too, and they are most often inflicted by the victim's mother. Bites can be on any part of the child's body, but the commonest sites are the arms, legs, buttocks and cheeks. The bites are not usually as severe as they are in cases of sexual assault, but they often leave a clear imprint of the attacker's teeth.

Multiple bite-marks found on the shoulders and arms are often self-inflicted, particularly in teenage girls.

There is huge variation in the nature of bite-marks. Human bites are usually distinguished by their semi-circular shape, whereas animal bites are of a much deeper U shape. Often the teeth of an attacker are set so close together that they leave behind two continuous curved lines, with no indication of separate teeth; other bites clearly show the marks of individual teeth, but as time passes the clear shapes blur and merge with each other. For that reason it is important that records be made as close to the time of an attack as possible.

Forensic technicians must take photographs of bite-marks in such a way that the resulting images will not tend to mislead. For example, although it is advisable always to photograph a bite or group of bites from various angles, there must be at least one clear view taken from a directly perpendicular angle, the plane of the film in the camera being parallel to the plane of the lesion; an accurate scale, showing measurements in centimetres and inches, should be included in the picture. Since bites are hardly ever on a flat surface there is bound to be some distortion of the view which is recorded, but a sufficient number of views, all taken at the same distance from the bite-mark, is usually reckoned to cut confusion or ambiguity to a minimum.

Sophisticated techniques of photography have sometimes proved more of a hindrance than a help, and at least one major stereoscopic system, designed for clinical photography, had to be shelved when it was discovered that a significant number of people could not make sense of the images it produced. Even a well-established technique like infra-red photography has shown itself to be an obstacle to clarity when recording bite-marks: it can show up bruising beneath the surface of the skin, but it can also show artefacts which obscure the field and generally tend to confuse the picture.

One of the less obvious hazards in photographing bite-marks is the use of lamps which heat the victim's skin. Heat will cause distortions in bite-mark patterns which can be severe enough to alter the shape of the lesion beyond recognition.

After photographs have been taken there is usually very little a technician or a pathologist can do about bite-marks without the supervision of a specialist. Sometimes an impression can be made from a deep bite-mark, although not many forensic technicians or pathologists have the necessary expertise. The procedure is to overlay the bite-mark with a liquid plastic material which hardens in the shape of the impression, creating a three-dimensional negative image of the lesion. Skin which is discovered at autopsy to be showing bite-marks can be cut out and soaked in formaldehyde to preserve it for examination by the forensic odontologist. Such specimens often shrink and distort, however, and they are usually of limited value.

When an on-the-spot evaluation of a bite-mark has to be made, and there are no striking dental features in the bite under study, most specialists believe it is pointless to try for an exact or near-exact match; the best thing to do is to try to exclude all suspects whose teeth obviously do not make the bite.

The following procedure is adopted in situations where more sophisticated examination methods are impossible. Different jurisdictions and different practitioners have varying requirements, but this is a core procedure.

The teeth of people who are suspects, or who could have been near the victim, are carefully examined. This has to be done with consent, and even if only one out of 20 suspects refuses, then the procedure has to be abandoned.

At examination, the following points have to be observed and all findings recorded.

- Is the subject wearing a denture? If he is, was he wearing it at the time of the attack?
- How many teeth in each jaw?
- Draw a diagram to show missing teeth.
- A description of any irregularity in the way the teeth are aligned, or in the way the upper and lower teeth meet.
- A note about teeth which have individual deformities or oddities of shape or position. A diagram if necessary.

When all of the foregoing has been done, and perhaps more, the forensic odontologist must bring his skills to bear on the evidence before him. Right at the start, when the difficult business of identifying a perpetrator is about to begin, the procedure will depend very much on which expert is going to attempt the identification. Some odontologists insist that the only way to make an identification is by excluding all the people who could not have made the bite-marks. Others will claim, just as firmly, that they can pinpoint the perpetrator by direct comparison of his teeth with the bite-marks. And that would not be the only point of difference between odontologists; there would be many.

The fact that the specialists can disagree, even at fundamental levels, is proof, in the view of some observers, that odontology is not a science at all. Its findings are open to wide interpretation – just like those of any branch of art. The reason for the latitude, it is argued, is that odontology (like a lot of other forensic specialities) has never been given an appropriate methodology. Its rules and procedures are too slack to merit the name of science.

That brings us back to Professor Michael Saks's assertion that DNA testing is the least problematic of the forensic sciences, in spite of what so many commentators say to the contrary.

As we saw in Chapter 2, the first British use of DNA analysis in a criminal investigation was in a case where two young women, at different times, were sexually assaulted and murdered, the first in 1983, the second three years later. A suspect in police custody confessed to the second murder but denied the first. Dr (now Professor) Alec Jeffries, who had devised the technique of DNA profiling (at that stage often referred to as 'DNA fingerprinting') was visited at Leicester University by senior police officers anxious to know if he could help establish whether there was a link, or not, between the murders of the two young women.

Dr Jeffries agreed to help. He performed a DNA analysis of material taken from the suspect held by the police. The results of the testing showed that the man was not the one who had sexually assaulted the first girl and so, by extension, had not killed her either. Jeffries also showed that both offences were committed by the same man.

Working from unpublished details of the two murders, the police were convinced the killer must be a local man; accordingly they invited some 5000 men from the vicinity of the crime scenes to volunteer samples of their blood. Using a mixture of blood group markers and multilocus DNA profiling, specialists in the technique managed to eliminate all 5000 volunteers. At that point the case did not look promising nor, in the view of many, did DNA profiling.

Then someone overheard a conversation in which a man admitted giving blood in place of one of the local villagers. The police were alerted and as a result a man called Colin Pitchfork was arrested. His blood was submitted to DNA profiling and was found to be a match to genetic material taken from the bodies of the two murder victims.

Some time later, in America, José Castro was accused of stabbing a mother and daughter to death. Blood was found on Castro's wristwatch; it was subjected to DNA profiling and reportedly matched the blood of one of the victims.

At a pre-trial hearing the DNA analysis, which had been performed by a commercial company, came under criticism on four main points:

1 standards guaranteeing the soundness of the evidence had not
   yet been established
2 assumptions made about population genetics were not known
   to be valid
3 the probabilities of random matches could not be shown to be
   correct
4 established guidelines for matching DNA bands had not been
   followed.

Because of the criticisms the prosecution and defence
scientists met to review the DNA evidence. After several hours they
issued a joint statement saying that the DNA information in the
Castro case was not reliable enough to back any conclusion as to
whether or not the samples matched. The prosecution were barred
from producing the DNA evidence in court.

The consequences of this action were far-reaching, and since
then forensic science laboratories have incorporated safeguards
and programmes of quality assurance which satisfy international
requirements. Overall, the case of José Castro began an important
series of moves towards regulating DNA profiling and making its
practitioners fall closer into line with general scientific practice.

The ironic outcome of this rigorous scrutiny and regulation of
DNA profiling, Saks points out, is that more is now known about the
strengths and weaknesses of the process than is known about
most of the older, more widely used forms of forensic science
evidence.

For much of the rest of forensic science, he says, we have yet to
get beyond the rough and bumpy starting phase. It is true that
ballistics, tool-marks evidence, fingerprinting, handwriting
identification and other disciplines have become accepted features
of forensic evidence in the courts, but none of them, Saks insists,
has undergone scrutiny even remotely as rigorous as that to which
DNA profiling is subjected. So much is taken for granted on the
basis of long-ago assumptions, made by authoritarians who were
not subject to criticism, and so much is therefore unproved,

idiosyncratic and in urgent need of exploration and correction. Good scientific practice demands nothing less.

The attention and scrutiny being given to DNA identification evidence, says Professor Saks, should be universally welcomed and encouraged. It is expected that rigorous investigation of DNA profiling will continue, and this process provides a model for the other forensic sciences. The expense of examining basic assumptions and procedures may be high, Saks says, but the hidden cost of making wrong assumptions and adopting faulty procedures is bound to be higher.

The scientific attitude is one which welcomes probing and debate, and good scientists are always willing to change in the face of fresh enlightenment. At present, the sciences which work in the service of justice offer very little solid support to back their claims of objectivity and open-mindedness.

'Forensic scientists,' says Professor Saks, 'like scientists in all other fields, should subject their claims to rigorous empirical tests. The results of these tests should be published and debated.'

Until such steps are taken, he adds, the police and the courts must view the claims of forensic scientists with far more caution than they have shown in the past.

A

alternative light imaging
171, 174, 177, 182
American Academy of
Forensic Sciences
(AAFS) 176-7, 178
American Board of
Forensic Odontology
(ABFO) 178-9
Andrews, Tommy Lee
31, 32
anthropometric technique
13

B

ballistics
ammunition 89-90
gun design 89
Bangladesh 126
Bertillon, Alphonse 13
Bertrand, Philippe 109-
10, 111, 113-14
Birmingham Six 158-9
bite-marks
in child abuse 182, 183
investigation
procedures 184-5
multiple bite-marks 183
photographing 183-4
in sexual attacks 182,
183
taking impressions 184
blood types 78
Bolivia 126-7, 132-3
brain scans 58-64
Brooks, Pierce R. 38
bullets and cartridge
cases 89-90
Bundy, Ted 18

C

Callaghan, Hugh 158
cartridge cases 89-90
Castro, José 175, 186-7
cellular telephone theft
93-8
child abuse 182, 183
Colombia 128-9, 133,
135-6
computer crime 114-22
computer viruses 119-
22
file-recovery programs
118-19
hackers 122
reluctance to prosecute

115, 117
computer databases
criminal data 38-9
DNA 7, 30-1, 33
fingerprints 7
Connolly, Dr John 45
counterfeiting 109, 113-
14
credit card fraud 109-14
gas chromatography
testing 112-13
holograms 111
magnetic coding 111-
12
profits 113-14
Tam case 109-11
crime detection, history of
12-14
crime-scene examination
contact traces 6, 13
SOCOs (Scene of Crime
Officers) 6
Crowley, Sid 55, 56, 61,
62, 63, 64, 65

D

Degarmo, Roger Leroy
41-3, 55-8, 60, 61,
63-6
diminished responsibility
48-9
DNA (deoxyribonucleic
acid) 169
DNA analysis
blood collection 34
corruptible material
34-5
criticisms 32-3, 187
databases 7, 30-1, 33
disputed profiles 32
DNA extraction 32
errors 34
hairs 35
identical profiles 33
of old material 35
polymerase chain
reaction (PCR)
technique 35-6
profiling 31-4, 169
scrutiny and regulation
of 9, 187-8
document examination
chemical analysis
101, 108
ESDA (Electrostatic
Detection

Apparatus)
technique 101-2,
108
FISH (Forensic
Information System
for Handwriting) 107
forged documents see
forgery
non-destructive
techniques 101
sub-specialities 107-8
Doyle, Sir Arthur Conan
13
drug crime 8-9, 125-54
couriers 125-6
drug chemists 146
drug law enforcement
134, 136, 147, 149
go-betweens 137
Latin American
connection 128-9,
130-4, 136
manufacturing
processes 144-6
profits 113, 126, 133
pushers 137
targeting the source
134-5
Drug Enforcement
Agency (DEA) 134, 136,
146
Drug-Free Workplace Act
1988 149
drug tests
employee testing 147-
9, 153, 154
hair testing 151-2, 153
immunoassay 148
mass-screening 147-9
mass spectrometry 148
urine testing 150-1,
152-3
drugs
addiction 128
cocaine 126-7, 128-9,
137, 141, 146
codeine 128
crack 145
designer drugs 140-4
DM; DET; DP; DIPT
143-4
DOB ('Bromo-STP')
143
Ecstasy (MDMA) 142-3
heroin 128, 129, 134-5,
136, 141

illegality of 129-30
Intellex (E4Euh) 143
marijuana 129
MDA 143
MMMP 142
morphine 127-8
opium 127
rebound episodes 138
recreational drugs 141
smart drugs 144

E
Erdmann, Ralph E. 158
ESDA (Electrostatic Detection Apparatus) technique 101-2, 108
expert witnesses 7, 32, 157, 160-1

F
FBI
  Behavioural Sciences Unit 17
  drug law enforcement 134
  murder, categorization of 17
  Uniform Crime Reports (UCRs) 17
fetishes 51, 52
fingerprints
  classification systems 13-15
  databases 7
  ninhydrin test 108-9
Finkle, Brian 149-50, 152, 153, 154
FISH (Forensic Information System for Handwriting) 107
forensic anthropology
  combined disciplines 77-8
  fundamental questions 76
  human skeleton 75, 78-86
  techniques 78
forensic odontology
  bite-marks 182-5
  defined 182
forensic science:
  criticisms of allegations of misconduct 161
  discredited tests and opinions 161-8

expert witness bias 160-1
flawed evidence 9, 158-9, 160
laboratory bottlenecks 159-60
negligence 160
passive defence 161
procedural costs 159
prosecution bias 160
forgery
  counterfeiting 109, 113-14
  expense claims 102-3
  fraudulent photocopies 107-8
  receipts 101-2
  signatures 100-1
  typewriter-related crime 103-6
Fox, J. 19, 20
Freud, Sigmund 157
Frye hearings 152

G
Galton-Henry fingerprint classification system 14
gas chromatography 112-13
Geiger, Ernst 36-7
Giles, Dr Audrey 99, 100-1, 102-3
Gladden, Greg 43, 56, 57, 58, 60, 61-2, 64-5, 66
Golden Crescent 135
Golden Triangle 135
Guatemala 8, 69-78, 86-9, 90-1
gun design 89
gunshot wounds 87

H
haematology 78
hair
  DNA analysis 35
  hair testing for drugs 151-2, 153
Harper, Jim 16, 37, 39
Harvey, Susie 170
Herrold, Lynn 16-17, 39
Hickey, Dr John 60-1, 64
Hill, Patrick 158
Hochmeister, Manfred 33, 36
Hodgkin, Dr Thomas 45

Homicide Act 1957 48-9
Huberty, James 18
human rights abuses 8, 71-7
human skeleton
  determining the age 83-4
  determining the height 84-5
  determining the sex 79-83
  skull 81-2
Hunter, Gerry 158
hydrostatic test 163-4

I
identification science 169-70
immunoassay 148
insanity 43
  diminished responsibility 48-9
  insanity defences 43-6
  legal concept 43
  McNaughton Rules 44, 47-8, 52
Institut für Rechtsmedizin 33

J
Jeffries, Professor Alec 31, 32, 35, 186
Jiminez, Pascuale 130-2
Jude Trust 137, 140

K
Kaufman, Andy 70, 71
Keko, Anthony 177, 179-81
Kirchner, Dr Robert 173
Knight, Professor Bernard 35

L
Lancaster, Ron 12, 30, 39
Levin, J. 19, 20
live birth, determining proof of 163-5
Long, Sherry 16, 30, 38
Lopez, Federico Reyes 70
Los Angeles Police Department (LAPD) 16, 37

M
'mad or bad' argument 7

Maguire, George 116-17
Mahayer, Helen 56
Manuel, Domingo 72, 74
Manuel, Juan 72, 74, 76
Manuel, Salvador 72
mass murderers 18, 19
Maxwell, Larry 170-1, 172, 175
Mayan Indians 69, 70
Mayberg, Dr Helen 59-60, 62-3, 66
McCrary, Agent Greg 39
McIlkenny, Richard 158
McNaughton, Daniel 45-6
McNaughton Rules 44, 47-8, 52
Moers, John 41, 42
Monro, Dr Edward Thomas 46
Montt, General Efraín Ríos 71-2, 77, 88-9, 90-1
Moon, Reverend Sun Myung 106-7
Morris, Ron 111, 113, 114
mortgage fraud 108
Moscoso, Fernando 70
multiple-victim killers
  case studies 20-9
  composite profile 19-20
  means of killing 19
  motives 19
  public perception of 19
  statistical information 18
  underlying patterns 29-30
  see also mass murderers; serial killers

N
ninhydrin test 108-9
novel scientific evidence 175

O
Office for National Drug Control Policy 149
Orego, Francisco 73
Oxford, Edward 44-5

P
paraphilia 51

Parker, Floyd 170
Parker, Mamie 170
Pearson, Karl 85
Perillo, Ben 134, 135, 136
Perlman, David 142
Peru 133
PET (Positron Emission Tomography) scans 58-64
Pitchfork, Colin 31, 186
Plan de Sanchez 70-7, 87-9, 90-1
Power, Billy 158
prostitute murder victims 12

R
radiocarbon dating 78
Reagan, Nancy 147
Reagan, Ronald 148
religious delusions 20, 22
Ressler, Special Agent Robert 17

S
Saks, Professor Michael 169, 170, 185, 187-8
Schmitt, Stefan 70
scientific misconduct 161
  serial killers
  forensic difficulties 6
  sexual murders 17, 18
  statistical information 18
  unknown motive category 18
sexual murders 17, 18
shoplifting 113
smart cards 114
smart drugs 144
Snow, Dr Clyde 8, 70-1, 73-4, 75, 76, 78, 79, 81, 86-7, 88, 90, 91
SOCOs (Scene of Crime Officers) 6, 159
Speck, Richard 18
Spooner, Mark 96-8, 123
status lymphaticus 162-3
Stead, Howard 146
strangulation, ligatures 16-17
Strickler, Kimberley Anne 41, 42, 55, 56

T
trace wound patterns 171, 173, 174, 175
typewriter-related crime 103-6
Tytell, Martin 103-6, 107
Tytell, Pearl 104, 106-7
Tytell, Peter 104, 106, 107

U
Unterweger, Jack 6, 36-8, 39

V
vagal inhibition 162
Valdizón, Mariana 70
VICAP (Violent Criminal Apprehension Program) database 38-9
Vick, Deputy Michael 171
victimology 7
Victoria, Queen 44, 46-7
Vucetich, Juan 14

W
Walker, John 158
Walker, Professor Nigel 43, 44, 48, 49, 52, 66-7
West, Dr Michael 170, 171-4, 175-81, 182
white-collar crime
  cellular telephone theft 93-8
computer crime 114-22
credit card fraud 109-14
forgery 98-109